HOLT SCIENCE & TECHNOLOGY

GRADE 6
Texas Edition

DIRECTED READING
WORKBOOK

HOLT, RINEHART AND WINSTON

A Harcourt Education Company

Austin · New York · Orlando · Atlanta · San Francisco · Boston · Dallas · Toronto · London

STAFF CREDITS

Director of Special Projects: Suzanne Thompson

Managing Editor: Joan Marie Lindsay

Senior Editor: Annie Hartnett

Editorial Coordinator: John Kendall

Editorial Assistant: Brian Howell

ISBN 0-03-067784-X

1 2 3 179 03 02 01

TABLE OF CONTENTS

ABOUT DIRECTED READING WORKSHEETS

These worksheets help students develop and practice fundamental reading comprehension skills. Completed **Directed Reading Worksheets** provide a comprehensive review tool for students to use when studying for an exam.

Correlation Of Directed Reading Worksheets and Texas Essential Knowledge and Skills

	*Science TEKS: Science Concepts and Scientific Process		*Science TEKS: Science Concepts and Scientific Process
Chapter 1	6.2A, 6.2B, 6.2C, 6.3A, 6.3B, 6.3C, 6.1A, 6.2E, 6.4A	**Chapter 12**	6.1A, 6.2A, 6.2B, 6.2C, 6.2E, 6.3C, 6.3D, 6.4A, 6.10C, 6.12B
Chapter 2	6.8A, 6.1A, 6.2B, 6.2C, 6.2D, 6.4A, 6.7A, 6.7B, 6.2A, 6.2E, 6.3D	**Chapter 13**	6.1A, 6.2B, 6.2E, 6.3C, 6.4A, 6.4B, 6.10A, 6.10C
Chapter 3	6.7B, 6.1A, 6.1B, 6.2A, 6.2B, 6.2C, 6.2D, 6.3C, 6.3E, 6.4A	**Chapter 14**	6.1A, 6.2A, 6.2B, 6.2C, 6.2D, 6.3A, 6.3C, 6.4A, 6.10A, 6.10C
Chapter 4	6.6A, 6.6B, 6.1A, 6.2A, 6.2B, 6.2C, 6.4A, 6.4B, 6.6A	**Chapter 15**	6.1A, 6.2A, 6.2B, 6.2C, 6.2D, 6.2E, 6.3A, 6.3C, 6.4A, 6.5A
Chapter 5	6.8A, 6.1A, 6.2A, 6.2B, 6.2C, 6.2D, 6.2E, 6.3C, 6.4A, 6.9A, 6.9B, 6.9C	**Chapter 16**	6.7B, 6.2B, 6.2C, 6.2E, 6.6C, 6.14A, 6.1A, 6.2B, 6.2C, 6.3C, 6.4A
Chapter 6	6.6A, 6.1A, 6.2A, 6.2B, 6.2C, 6.2D, 6.4A, 6.9A, 6.9B,	**Chapter 17**	6.6C, 6.7B, 6.2B, 6.2C, 6.2E, 6.6A, 6.1A, 6.2D, 6.3C, 6.4A6.1B
Chapter 7	6.10B, 6.11B, 6.1A, 6.2B, 6.2D, 6.2E, 6.3C, 6.4A, 6.10A, 6.2C	**Chapter 18**	6.5A, 6.6C, 6.8B, 6.1A, 6.2A, 6.2B, 6.2C, 6.2E, 6.3C, 6.4A, 6.14B, 6.1B
Chapter 8	6.2A, 6.2B, 6.2C, 6.2D, 6.2E, 6.3C, 6.4A, 6.11A, 6.11C	**Chapter 19**	6.14C, 6.1A, 6.2B, 6.2C, 6.3B, 6.4A, 6.3A, 6.2A, 6.2D, 6.3C
Chapter 9	6.12B, 6.1A, 6.2B, 6.12A, 6.2C, 6.2D, 6.2E, 6.4A	**Chapter 20**	6.5A, 6.5B, 6.13A, 6.3A, 6.4A, 6.1A, 6.2C, 6.2D, 6.3C
Chapter 10	6.8C, 6.12C, 6.1A, 6.2A, 6.4A	**Chapter 21**	6.5A, 6.13A, 6.2A, 6.2C, 6.3C, 6.4A
Chapter 11	6.2B, 6.2E, 6.4A, 6.2C		

*Some TEKs reflect partial coverage.

CHAPTER

1 **DIRECTED READING WORKSHEET**

Science in Our World

As you read Chapter 1, which begins on page 2 of your textbook, answer the following questions.

What Is That? (p. 2)

1. When you first looked at the illustration on these two pages, what did you think the pictured objects were?

_____

_____

_____

_____

Pre-Reading Questions (p. 2)

Answer these questions in your ScienceLog now. Then later, you'll have a chance to revise your answers based on what you've learned.

Start-Up Activity (p. 3)

2. What is the seemingly impossible problem in this activity?

_____

_____

_____

Section 1: Science and Scientists (p. 4)

3. What are the first steps of being a scientist?

_____

_____

_____

_____

Science Starts with a Question (p. 4)

4. How is the student in Figure 1 being a scientist?

_____

_____

Investigation: The Search for Answers (p. 5)

5. How can you look for answers to scientific questions? (Circle all that apply.)

    a. make careful observations   **c.** ask a friend

    b. do research   **d.** do an experiment

6. Using the Internet is not a valid way to do research.

    True or False? (Circle one.)

Why Ask Why? (p. 6)

7. Paper can be _____ to save trees.

8. Why do lighter cars reduce air pollution?

_____

_____

_____

_____

_____

Scientists Are All Around You (p. 7)

Match each science-related job in Column B to its job description in Column A, and write the corresponding letter in the space provided.

Column A	Column B
_____ **9.** makes maps of the surface of the Earth	**a.** environmental scientist
_____ **10.** studies how humans interact with their environment	**b.** cartographer
_____ **11.** puts scientific knowledge to practical use by designing and building things	**c.** engineer

Section Review (p. 8)

Now that you've finished Section 1, review what you learned by answering the Section Review questions in your ScienceLog.

Section 2: Scientific Methods (p. 9)

1. The most common meat-eating creature during the Jurassic period

    was the _____ .

You Feel the Earth Move (p. 9)

2. What is causing the booming noise and the shaking ground?

_____

_____

_____

_____

What Are Scientific Methods? (p. 10)

3. Scientists use scientific methods to

_____ questions and

_____ problems by following a series

of _____ .

4. Look at the flowchart in Figure 9. If the conclusions that you draw do not support your hypothesis, what are three things that you might do next?

_____

_____

_____

Ask a Question (p. 11)

5. Scientists often ask a question after they make many observations.

True or False? (Circle one.)

6. _____ are observations that are made with tools.

Form a Hypothesis (p. 12)

7. A hypothesis is

   a. not based on observations.
   b. usually stated in an "if. . . then. . ." format.
   c. a possible explanation or answer to a question.
   d. best when it is untestable.

Mid-Section Review (p. 12)

Now that you've finished the first part of Section 2, review what you learned by answering the Mid-Section Review questions in your ScienceLog.

Chapter 1 Directed Reading, continued

Test the Hypothesis (p. 13)

8. Scientists test hypotheses by gathering _____ .

9. What is a controlled experiment?

_____

_____

Analyze the Results (p. 13)

10. Scientists often make tables and graphs to arrange their data.

True or False? (Circle one.)

Draw Conclusions (p. 14)

11. Which of the following is NOT true when drawing a conclusion?

  a. The results may support the hypothesis.

  b. The results may disprove the hypothesis.

  c. The results may lead scientists to ask new questions and form new hypotheses.

  d. none of the above

Communicate Results (p. 14)

Review pages 11–14 again. Given below in Column A are descriptions of tasks that Dr. Gillette performed in his scientific investigation. Choose the step of the scientific method in Column B that best matches the description in Column A, and write the corresponding letter in the space provided.

Column A	Column B
____ **12.** found that the bones were too large or too different in shape to come from any known dinosaur	**a.** Ask a question.
____ **13.** concluded that the bones were from a yet unknown dinosaur	**b.** Form a hypothesis.
____ **14.** measured the bones and compared the measurements with those of bones from known dinosaurs	**c.** Test the hypothesis. **d.** Analyze the results.
____ **15.** shared his discovery in a press conference and in a report	**e.** Draw conclusions.
____ **16.** wondered what kind of dinosaur the bones came from	**f.** Communicate results.
____ **17.** thought the bones came from a kind of dinosaur not yet known to scientists	

18. Was Dr. Gillette's work on *Seismosaurus hallorum* finished after he communicated his results? Explain.

_____

_____

_____

_____

Section Review (p. 15)

Now that you've finished Section 2, review what you learned by answering the Section Review questions in your ScienceLog.

Section 3: Scientific Models (p. 16)

1. You can use baking soda, clay, and _____ to build a model of a volcano.

Types of Scientific Models (p. 16)

2. You can represent an _____ or

_____ by using a model.

3. How do you think a model volcano, such as the one shown in Figure 15, might help you understand a real volcano?

_____

_____

_____

_____

4. A conceptual model is made up of mathematical equations

and data. True or False? (Circle one.)

Models Are Just the Right Size (p. 18)

Decide whether a useful model for each of the following would be larger or smaller than the actual object, and write the appropriate answer in the space provided.

5. a skyscraper _____

6. a computer chip _____

7. the Earth _____

Models Build Scientific Knowledge (p. 18)

8. A unifying _____ for a broad range of
hypotheses and observations that have been supported by

_____ is called a theory.

Mark each of the following statements *True* or *False*.

9. _____ A scientific law tells you how to behave.

10. _____ Laws tell you *why* something happens, not *what* happens.

11. _____ A scientific law is a summary of many experimental
results and observations.

Section Review (p. 19)

Now that you've finished Section 3, review what you learned by
answering the Section Review questions in your ScienceLog.

Section 4: Tools, Measurement, and Safety (p. 20)

1. A _____ is anything that helps you do a task.

Tools for Seeing (p. 20)

2. What do microscopes help you do?

_____

_____

_____

3. A compound light microscope is made up of a

_____ , a stage, and a tube with lenses at
each end.

Tools for Measuring (p. 21)

4. What tool is used to measure mass?
  a. a meterstick
  b. a spring scale
  c. a balance
  d. a thermometer

Tools for Analyzing (p. 21)

5. You could use a calculator to help you analyze scientific data.

True or False? (Circle one.)

Chapter 1 Directed Reading, continued

Measurement (p. 22)

6. At one time in England, the standard for _____ was three grains of barley placed end to end.

7. Many standardized units of measurement were originally based on parts of the human body. True or False? (Circle one.)

8. Identify one advantage of using SI measurements.

_____

_____

_____

_____

_____

_____

_____

9. Which unit of measure is most practical for measuring the length of your arm?

    a. kilometer (km)   **c.** micrometer (μm)

    b. meter (m)   **d.** nanometer (nm)

10. What equation would you use to calculate how much carpet is needed to cover the floor of your classroom?

_____

11. The units for area are called _____ units.

12. Before you can determine how many hippos will fit into a cage, you need two pieces of information. What are they?

_____

_____

_____

_____

13. Which of the following is NOT a valid unit of measurement for volume?

    a. square micrometer (μm^2)   **c.** milliliter (mL)

    b. cubic centimeter (cm^3)   **d.** liter (L)

14. Would you describe the mass of sacks of grain in grams? Why or why not? If not, which unit would you use?

_____

_____

_____

_____

_____

15. Look at Figure 26 on page 25. Water boils at 212° _____

or 100° _____ .

Safety Rules (p. 25)

Match the symbol with the appropriate label, and write the corresponding letter in the space provided.

_____ **16.** hand safety

_____ **17.** sharp object   **a.**

_____ **18.** clothing protection   **b.**

_____ **19.** chemical safety   **c.**

_____ **20.** eye protection   **d.**

_____ **21.** electric safety   **e.**

_____ **22.** plant safety   **f.**

_____ **23.** heating safety   **g.**

_____ **24.** animal safety   **h.**

                                     i.

Section Review (p. 25)

Now that you've finished Section 4, review what you learned by answering the Section Review questions in your ScienceLog.

CHAPTER

2   **DIRECTED READING WORKSHEET**

The Properties of Matter

As you read Chapter 2, which begins on page 36 of your textbook, answer the following questions.

Nice Ice (p. 36)

1. Look at the photograph on pages 36 and 37. How does what you see compare with steam rising from a kettle or dew collecting on grass?

_____

_____

_____

_____

Pre-Reading Questions (p. 36)

Answer these questions in your ScienceLog now. Then later, you'll have a chance to revise your answers based on what you've learned.

Start-Up Activity (p. 37)

2. What will you do in this activity?

_____

_____

_____

_____

Section 1: What Is Matter? (p. 38)

3. What do a human, hot soup, and a neon sign have in common?

_____

_____

Everything Is Made of Matter (p. 38)

4. Matter is anything that has _____ and

_____ .

Matter Has Volume (p. 38)

Answer each of the following statements *True* or *False*.

5. _____ An object's volume is the amount of space the object takes up.

6. _____ Because things have volume, they can't share the same space at the same time.

7. _____ A liquid's volume is usually expressed in grams or milligrams.

8. _____ When you measure a volume of water in a graduated cylinder, you should look at the bottom of the meniscus.

9. The volume of solid objects is expressed in

_____ units.

10. What three dimensions do you need in order to find the volume of a rectangular solid object?

_____

_____

_____

_____

11. You can measure the volume of any solid object by measuring

_____

_____

Matter Has Mass (p. 41)

12. Why do you have more mass than a peanut?

_____

_____

13. Weight is a measure of the gravitational force exerted on an object. True or False? (Circle one.)

14. An object weighs _____ on the moon than it does on Earth.

15. The basic SI unit for _____ is the kilogram. The unit for _____ is the newton.

16. Why is it easier to push a grocery cart than a car? Explain in terms of mass and inertia.

_____

_____

_____

_____

_____

Section Review (p. 42)

Now that you've finished Section 1, review what you learned by answering the Section Review questions in your ScienceLog.

Section 2: Describing Matter (p. 43)

1. In a game of 20 Questions, the most helpful questions you can

ask are about the _____ of the object.

Physical Properties (p. 43)

2. Which physical properties is the boy in the picture on page 43 asking about?

_____

_____

_____

Match each physical property in Column B to the correct phrase in Column A, and write the corresponding letter in the appropriate space. Use Figure 7 on pages 44–45 to help you.

Column A	Column B
_____ **3.** A flavored drink mix dissolves in water.	**a.** state
_____ **4.** Aluminum can be rolled into sheets to make foil.	**b.** thermal conductivity
_____ **5.** Ice is the solid form of water.	**c.** solubility
_____ **6.** Copper can be pulled into wire.	**d.** density
_____ **7.** A foam cup protects your hand from being burned by the hot chocolate in the cup.	**e.** ductility
_____ **8.** Lead is used to make sinkers for fishing line.	**f.** malleability

▲ CHAPTER 2

9. What will happen if you shake the graduated cylinder in Figure 9? Explain.

_____

_____

_____

_____

_____

_____

_____

10. Is 40 mL of oil denser than 25 mL of vinegar? _____

11. Density depends on the amount of substance you have.

True or False? (Circle one.)

12. In the formula for density, D means _____,

V stands for _____ , and m stands for

_____ .

13. Using the table on page 46, list the substances mercury, water, gold, and oxygen from the densest to the least dense.

_____

Mid-Section Review (p. 46)

Now that you've finished the first part of Section 2, review what you've learned by answering the Mid-Section Review questions in your ScienceLog.

Chemical Properties (p. 47)

14. A chemical property describes matter based on its ability to

remain unchanged. True or False? (Circle one.)

15. The word *reactivity* refers to the ability of two or more substances

to combine and form a new substance. True or False? (Circle one.)

16. In Figure 10 on page 47, why isn't there rust on the bumper of the car?

_____

_____

_____

_____

17. In Figure 11 on page 48, the grainy texture of wood is an

example of a _____ property.

18. Characteristic properties help scientists to identify and classify substances. True or False? (Circle one.)

Physical Changes Don't Form New Substances (p. 48)
19. What is a physical change?

_____

_____

_____

_____

20. If you make a physical change to a substance, the identity of the substance changes. True or False? (Circle one.)

21. Give an example of how a physical change does not change the identity of the matter involved.

_____

_____

_____

_____

_____

_____

_____

_____

Chapter 2 Directed Reading, continued

Chemical Changes Form New Substances (p. 49)

22. A chemical _____ describes a substance's
ability to go through a chemical change. A chemical

_____ happens when two or more
substances are changed into one or more new substances.

23. How do you know that baking a cake involves chemical changes?

_____

_____

_____

_____

24. In Figure 14, the odor of soured milk indicates that a chemical

change has taken place. True or False? (Circle one.)

25. What clues signal a chemical change? (Circle all that apply.)
   a. fizzing and foaming
   b. production of sound or light
   c. changes in color
   d. heat
   e. none of the above

26. Some chemical changes can be reversed with more chemical

changes. True or False? (Circle one.)

Section Review (p. 51)

Now that you've finished Section 2, review what you learned by
answering the Section Review questions in your ScienceLog.

Chapter 3 Directed Reading, continued

Melting: Solids to Liquids (p. 71)

7. Could you use gallium to make jewelry? Why or why not?

_____

_____

_____

_____

8. The melting point of a substance is a characteristic property because it is the same for different amounts of the same substance. True or False? (Circle one.)

9. During a(n) _____ change, energy is gained by a substance as it changes state.

Freezing: Liquids to Solids (p. 71)

10. The freezing point of a substance is the temperature at which it changes from a _____ to a

_____ .

11. What happens if energy is added or removed from the ice water in Figure 13?

_____

_____

12. Freezing is an exothermic change because _____ is removed from the substance as it changes state.

Vaporization: Liquids to Gases (p. 72)

Choose the term in Column B that best matches the description in Column A, and write the corresponding letter in the space provided.

Column A	Column B
____ **13.** vaporization at the surface of a liquid below its boiling point	**a.** boiling point
____ **14.** the change of state from a liquid to a gas	**b.** vaporization
____ **15.** vaporization that occurs throughout a liquid	**c.** steam
____ **16.** the product of vaporization of liquid water	**d.** evaporation
____ **17.** temperature at which a liquid boils	**e.** boiling

CHAPTER 3

Condensation: Gases to Liquids (p. 73)

Mark each of the following statements *True* or *False*.

18. _____ At a given pressure, the condensation point of a substance is the same as its melting point.

19. _____ For a substance to change from a gas to a liquid, particles must clump together.

20. _____ Condensation is an exothermic change.

Sublimation: Solids to Gases (p. 74)

21. Solid carbon dioxide isn't ice. So why is it called "dry ice"?

_____

_____

_____

22. The change of state from a solid to a _____ is called sublimation. Energy must be added for sublimation to

occur, so it is an _____ change.

Comparing Changes of State (p. 74)

23. Look at the table on page 74. Which two changes of state occur at the same temperature?

a. condensation and melting   **c.** vaporization and condensation

b. sublimation and freezing   **d.** melting and vaporization

Change in Temperature Versus Change of State (p. 75)

24. Temperature is related to the speed of particles.

True or False? (Circle one.)

25. A substance can undergo changes in temperature and in state at

the same time. True or False? (Circle one.)

Mark each of the following statements *True* or *False*.

26. _____ The speed of the particles in a substance changes when the temperature changes.

27. _____ The temperature of a substance changes before the change of state is complete.

Section Review (p. 75)

Now that you've finished Section 2, review what you learned by answering the Section Review questions in your ScienceLog.

CHAPTER

4 DIRECTED READING WORKSHEET

Matter in Motion

As you read Chapter 4, which begins on page 84 of your textbook, answer the following questions.

Slick Speed (p. 84)

1. What does it take to be a good speedskater?

_____

_____

_____

_____

_____

_____

Pre-Reading Questions (p. 84)

Answer these questions in your ScienceLog now. Then later, you'll have a chance to revise your answers based on what you've learned.

Start-Up Activity (p. 85)

2. What do you predict this activity will demonstrate?

_____

_____

_____

Section 1: Measuring Motion (p. 86)

3. Name something in motion that you can't see moving.

_____

_____

_____

Observing Motion (p. 86)

4. To determine if an object is in motion, compare its position over

time in relation to a _____ point.

CHAPTER 4

5. Buildings, trees, and mountains are all useful reference points. Why?

_____

_____

_____

6. Can a moving object be used as a reference point? Explain.

_____

_____

_____

_____

Speed Depends on Distance and Time (p. 87)

Each of the following statements is false. Change the underlined word to make the statement true. Write the new word in the space provided.

7. <u>Motion</u> is the rate at which an object moves.

_____

8. How fast an object moves depends on the distance traveled and the <u>road</u> taken to travel that distance.

_____

9. The SI unit for speed is <u>km/h</u>.

_____

10. Why is it useful to calculate average speed?

_____

_____

11. Write out in words how to calculate average speed.

_____

_____

_____

Chapter 4 Directed Reading, continued

12. Look at the Brain Food on p. 87. Suppose a car travels 250 m in 10 seconds. Is its average speed greater than or less than that of a running cheetah?

_____

_____

_____

_____

Velocity: Direction Matters (p. 88)

13. Look at the riddle on page 88. Why don't the birds end up at the same place?

_____

_____

14. Velocity has speed and _____ .

15. Which of the following does NOT experience a change in velocity?

   a. A motorcyclist applies the brakes while driving down a straight street.
   b. An experimental car switches from gasoline to electric power while maintaining the same speed and direction.
   c. A baseball player running from first base to second base at 10 m/s comes to a stop in 1.5 seconds.
   d. A bus traveling at a constant speed turns a corner.

16. To find the resultant velocity, add velocities that are in

_____ direction(s), or subtract velocities

that are in _____ direction(s).

Acceleration: The Rate at Which Velocity Changes (p. 89)

17. Why can you say you accelerate as you slow down and swerve to avoid hitting a rock when inline skating?

_____

_____

_____

_____

► ► CHAPTER 4
▲

Chapter 4 Directed Reading, continued

18. Another name for acceleration in which speed increases is

_____ acceleration.

19. Negative acceleration, or acceleration in which speed

decreases, is also called _____ .

20. Write the formula for calculating average acceleration in the space below.

21. Scientifically speaking, how do you know the cyclist in Figure 3 on page 90 is accelerating?

_____

_____

_____

_____

_____

_____

22. When you are standing completely still, you are experiencing

acceleration. True or False? (Circle one.)

23. What kind of acceleration is taking place in Figure 4 on page 91?

_____

24. How can you recognize acceleration on a graph?
   a. The graph shows distance versus time.
   b. The graph shows time versus distance.
   c. The graph is a curve showing velocity versus time.
   d. The graph is a straight line.

Section Review (p. 91)

Now that you've finished Section 1, review what you learned by answering the Section Review questions in your ScienceLog.

Section 2: What Is a Force? (p. 92)

Mark the following statements *True* or *False*.

1. _____ A force is a push or a pull.

2. _____ All forces have size and direction.

3. _____ Forces are expressed in liters.

Forces Act on Objects (p. 92)

4. You can exert a push without an object to receive the push.

True or False? (Circle one.)

5. Name three examples of objects that you exert forces on when you are doing your schoolwork.

_____

_____

_____

_____

_____

6. In which of the following situations is a force being exerted? (Circle all that apply.)

a. A woman pushes an elevator button.
b. A pile of soil sits on the ground.
c. Socks like the ones in Figure 6, page 93, cling together when they have just come out of the dryer.
d. Magnets stick to a refrigerator.

Forces in Combination (p. 93)

7. In Figure 7 on page 93, how does the net force help the students move the piano?

_____

_____

_____

_____

_____

_____

CHAPTER 4

8. Suppose the dog on the left in Figure 8, page 94, pulled with a force of 13 N. Which dog would win the tug of war? Explain.

_____

_____

_____

_____

Unbalanced and Balanced Forces (p. 94)

9. Why is it useful to know the net force?

_____

_____

_____

_____

10. Forces are unbalanced when the net force on an object is not

equal to _____ .

11. To start or change the motion of an object, you need a(n)

_____ force.

12. Forces are _____ when the net force applied to an object is zero.

13. Are the forces on the cards in Figure 9 balanced? How do you know?

_____

_____

_____

Section Review (p. 95)

Now that you've finished Section 2, review what you learned by answering the Section Review questions in your ScienceLog.

Section 3: Friction: A Force That Opposes Motion (p. 96)

1. What force causes a moving ball to slow down?

_____

_____

The Source of Friction (p. 96)

2. Friction occurs when the microscopic hills and valleys of two surfaces stick together. True or False? (Circle one.)

3. The ground creates more friction than ice. Why is that?

_____

_____

4. Why is more force needed to slide the larger book in Figure 11 on page 97?

_____

_____

_____

_____

_____

5. If you change how much of one surface touches the other surface, the amount of friction changes. True or False? (Circle one.)

Types of Friction (p. 97)

Match each type of friction in Column B with its example in Column A, and write the corresponding letter in the space provided.

Column A	Column B
____ **6.** an eraser stops moving across a desk	**a.** sliding friction
____ **7.** a crate being pushed but not moving up a loading ramp	**b.** rolling friction
____ **8.** a wheeled cart being pushed	**c.** fluid friction
____ **9.** air rushing past a speeding car	**d.** static friction

10. Static friction is at work when you try to push a heavy block across a table and the block _____ .

11. As soon as an object starts moving, static friction

_____ .

Friction Can Be Harmful or Helpful (p. 99)

12. How does friction harm the engine of a car?

_____

_____

_____

_____

13. Which of the following are ways to reduce friction?
(Circle all that apply.)

   a. Use a lubricant.

   b. Change sliding friction to rolling friction.

   c. Push surfaces together.

   d. Make the surfaces that are rubbing against each other smoother.

Section Review (p. 100)

Now that you've finished Section 3, review what you learned by answering the Section Review questions in your ScienceLog.

Section 4: Gravity: A Force of Attraction (p. 101)

1. The force of attraction between two objects due to their masses

is _____ .

2. Why did the astronauts bounce on the moon?

_____

_____

All Matter Is Affected by Gravity (p. 101)

3. Does all matter experience gravity? Explain.

_____

_____

_____

4. The force that pulls you toward your pencil is

_____ force.

5. Look at the Biology Connection on page 101. Astronauts have grown seedlings during space shuttle missions to see how seeds

respond to changes in gravity. True or False? (Circle one.)

Chapter 4 Directed Reading, continued

---

6. All objects are attracted to each other due to gravitational force. So, why can't you see objects moving toward each other?

_____

_____

_____

_____

7. How are objects around us affected by the mass of the Earth?

_____

_____

_____

_____

The Law of Universal Gravitation (p. 102)

8. What connection did Newton make between the moon and a falling apple?

_____

_____

_____

9. Newton's law of universal gravitation describes the relationships between all of the following EXCEPT

   a. distance.   **c.** heat.
   b. mass.   **d.** gravitational force.

10. Which of the following objects are subject to the law of universal gravitation? (Circle all that apply.)

   a. satellites   **c.** frogs
   b. water   **d.** stars

11. If the distance between the objects is the same, the gravitational force between two feathers is greater than the gravitational force between two bowling balls. True or False? (Circle one.)

12. Why is a cat easier to pick up than an elephant?

_____

_____

_____

▲ CHAPTER 4

Chapter 4 Directed Reading, continued

---

13. Read the Astronomy Connection on page 103. In a

_____ , gravity is so great that even light

can't escape.

14. Why doesn't the sun's gravitational force pull you off Earth?

_____

_____

_____

15. What would happen to Earth and the other planets in the solar
system without the sun's gravitational force?

_____

_____

_____

Weight Is a Measure of Gravitational Force (p. 104)

16. The measure of the gravitational force on an object is the

object's _____ .

Identify each of the following statements as describing mass or
weight. Write M for mass and W for weight.

17. _____ different on the moon

18. _____ expressed in newtons

19. _____ can be expressed in kilograms

20. _____ measure of gravitational force

21. _____ value doesn't change

22. _____ amount of matter in an object

23. On Earth, mass and weight are constant, which means they are

the same thing. True or False? (Circle one.)

Section Review (p. 105)

Now that you've finished Section 4, review what you learned by
answering the Section Review questions in your ScienceLog.

CHAPTER

5 **DIRECTED READING WORKSHEET**

Energy and Energy Resources

As you read Chapter 5, which begins on page 116 of your textbook, answer the following questions.

The Race Is On! (p. 116)

1. Why would you need to worry about sunshine if you were going to be a driver in this race?

_____

_____

_____

_____

_____

Pre-Reading Questions (p. 116)

Answer these questions in your ScienceLog now. Then later, you'll have a chance to revise your answers based on what you've learned.

Start-Up Activity (p. 117)

2. How will you learn about energy in this activity?

_____

_____

Section 1: What Is Energy? (p. 118)

3. Where do you think energy is being transferred as the tennis game is played?

_____

_____

_____

Energy and Work—Working Together (p. 118)

4. Energy is the _____ to do work.

5. When you hit a tennis ball with a racket, energy is transferred from the racket to the ball. True or False? (Circle one.)

6. Energy is measured in _____ .

CHAPTER 5

7. Which of the following have kinetic energy?
(Circle all that apply.)

    a. a ball flying over a net   **c.** a moving car

    b. a moving tortoise   **d.** a parked car

8. The amount of kinetic energy a moving object has depends on its

_____ and _____ .

9. Which of the following is NOT true of kinetic energy?

    a. The faster something moves, the more kinetic energy it has.

    b. The lower the mass is, the higher the kinetic energy.

    c. Speed has a greater effect on kinetic energy than mass has.

    d. none of the above

Potential Energy Is Energy of Position (p. 120)

10. Why does a wound-up rubber band have potential energy?

_____

_____

_____

_____

11. What two measurements do you multiply together to find an object's gravitational potential energy?

_____

_____

_____

Forms of Energy (p. 121)

12. The total potential energy of all the particles in an object is

known as thermal energy. True or False? (Circle one.)

13. In Figure 4, on page 121, the particles in ocean water have less energy than the particles in steam. Why?

_____

_____

_____

_____

_____

Choose the type of energy in Column B that best matches the definition in Column A, and write the corresponding letter in the space provided. The type of energy may be used more than once.

Column A	Column B
____ **14.** energy caused by the vibrations of electrically charged particles	**a.** chemical
____ **15.** energy stored in a substance that can be released when the substance reacts	**b.** electrical
____ **16.** energy caused by an object's vibrations	**c.** sound
____ **17.** energy of moving electrons	**d.** light
____ **18.** energy used to cook food in a microwave	

19. Which of the following forms of energy would you find in your kitchen? (Circle all that apply.)

   a. electrical   **c.** nuclear

   b. light   **d.** sound

20. Nuclear energy gives the sun its energy. True or False? (Circle one.)

21. Nuclear energy can be produced only by splitting the nucleus of an atom. True or False? (Circle one.)

22. Where does the sun get its energy to light and heat the Earth?

_____

_____

_____

_____

_____

23. The nucleus of an atom can store _____ energy.

Section Review (p. 123)

Now that you've finished Section 1, review what you learned by answering the Section Review questions in your ScienceLog.

Section 2: Energy Conversions (p. 124)

1. An energy conversion can happen between any two forms of energy. True or False? (Circle one.)

▲ ▲ **CHAPTER 5**

From Kinetic to Potential and Back (p. 124)

Take a look at Figure 10, on page 124. Mark each of the following energy conversions K→P (kinetic to potential) or P→K (potential to kinetic).

2. _____ You jump down, and the trampoline stretches.

3. _____ The trampoline does work on you, and you bounce up.

4. _____ You reach the top of your jump on the trampoline.

5. _____ You are about to hit the trampoline again.

6. In Figure 11, on page 125, the potential energy of the pendulum is the smallest at which point in its swing?

    a. the top of the swing   **c.** the slowest point

    b. the bottom of the swing   **d.** none of the above

7. What is mechanical energy?

_____

_____

Conversions Involving Chemical Energy (p. 125)

8. Why does eating breakfast give you energy to start the day?

_____

_____

_____

_____

9. The energy you get from food originally comes from the sun.

True or False? (Circle one.)

10. During _____, plants convert light energy into chemical energy.

Conversions Involving Electrical Energy (p. 127)

11. When you turn on a hair dryer, electrical energy is converted into which of the following forms of energy? (Circle all that apply.)

    a. nuclear energy   **c.** kinetic energy

    b. sound energy   **d.** thermal energy

12. In a battery, _____ energy is converted into _____ energy.

Conservation of Energy (p. 128)

13. A roller-coaster car never returns to its starting height because energy gets lost along the way.

True or False? (Circle one.)

14. Where does friction oppose motion on a roller-coaster car? (Circle all that apply.)

  a. between the wheels of the car and the track
  b. between the car and the surrounding air
  c. between the passenger and the track
  d. between the car and the passenger

15. Some of the original amount of potential energy of a roller-coaster car is converted into kinetic energy on the way down the first hill, and some of the energy is changed to

_____ energy.

16. The potential energy of the car at the top of the second hill of a roller coaster is equal to the original potential energy of the car at the top of the first hill.

True or False? (Circle one.)

17. The law of conservation of energy states that energy can be neither

_____ nor _____.

18. The total amount of energy in a closed system is

_____.

19. A roller coaster is part of a closed system. List the other parts.

_____

_____

Energy Conversions and Efficiency (p. 129)

20. During an energy conversion, energy is rarely converted to

thermal energy. True or False? (Circle one.)

21. What does energy efficiency compare?

_____

_____

_____

22. The smooth shape of newer cars reduces friction between the cars and the air. Because these cars move through the air more easily,

they are more efficient. True or False? (Circle one.)

CHAPTER 5

23. Why is it impossible to make a perpetual motion machine?

_____

_____

_____

_____

_____

_____

_____

_____

Section Review (p. 129)

Now that you've finished Section 2, review what you learned by answering the Section Review questions in your ScienceLog.

Section 3: Using Energy (p. 130)

1. Energy _____ help make energy useful to you.

Energy and Machines (p. 130)

2. How does a machine make work easier? (Circle all that apply.)

   a. by changing the direction of force needed to do work
   b. by changing the size of force needed to do work
   c. by requiring no force
   d. by increasing the amount of energy transferred

3. A machine can transfer more energy than you transfer to the machine. True or False? (Circle one.)

4. Which of the following kinetic energy transfers does NOT occur when you ride a bike as in Figure 17 on page 130?

   a. from legs to pedals   **c.** from chain to back wheel
   b. from pedals to chain   **d.** from gear wheel to chain

5. A digital alarm clock, a telephone, and a lawn mower are machines that perform _____ .

6. As gasoline burns inside a car's engine, _____ energy is converted into thermal and mechanical energy.

Heating and Cooling Systems (p. 132)

7. A warm-air heating system works like a hot-water heating system

except that _____ is used in place of water.

8. In a hot-water heating system, like the one shown in Figure 19 on

page 132, radiators transfer _____
energy to the surrounding air.

9. Which of the following is NOT a component of a passive solar heating system?

    a. large south-facing windows   **c.** moving parts

    b. thick walls   **d.** good insulation

10. Where is water heated in an active solar heating system?

_____

_____

Cooling Systems (p. 134)

11. Cooling systems move _____ energy out
of a warm area, so that it feels cooler.

12. A refrigerator is cool inside because it constantly moves

    a. thermal energy from the condenser coils on the outside of the refrigerator to the inside of the refrigerator.

    b. electrical energy from the condenser coils on the outside of the refrigerator to the inside of the refrigerator.

    c. thermal energy from inside the refrigerator to the condenser coils on the outside of the refrigerator.

    d. electrical energy from inside the refrigerator to the condenser coils on the outside of the refrigerator.

Section Review (p. 135)

Now that you've finished Section 3, review what you learned by answering the Section Review questions in your Sciencelog.

Section 4: Energy Resources (p. 136)

1. How do we use energy resources?

_____

_____

_____

_____

_____

CHAPTER 5

Chapter 5 Directed Reading, continued

2. The _____ is the source of most energy resources on Earth.

Nonrenewable Resources (p. 136)

3. Which of the following are fossil fuels? (Circle all that apply.)

    a. coal   **c.** petroleum

    b. wood   **d.** natural gas

4. Fossil fuels are formed from the buried remains of plants and animals that lived millions of years ago. True or False? (Circle one.)

5. Explain why fossil fuels are concentrated forms of the sun's energy.

_____

_____

_____

_____

_____

_____

Use the images on page 137 to answer questions 6–8.

6. Most of the coal supply in the United States is used for heating. True or False? (Circle one.)

7. Which of the following is NOT a petroleum product?

    a. gasoline   **c.** petrochemicals

    b. wax   **d.** wood

8. The cleanest-burning fossil fuel is _____ .

9. In the United States, _____ are the main source of electrical energy.

10. Take a moment to study Figure 25 on page 138. Put the following events in the correct sequence for the conversion of chemical energy in fossil fuels into electrical energy by writing the appropriate number in the space provided.

_____ A large magnet spins within a ring of wire coils, creating electric current.

_____ Thermal energy converts liquid water to steam.

_____ Electrical energy can be sent to homes and businesses.

_____ Fossil fuels are burned.

_____ Steam pushes against the blades of a turbine.

_____ Water is pumped into a boiler.

Chapter 5 Directed Reading, continued

11. One of the uranium fuel pellets shown in Figure 26 on page 139 has

the energy equivalent of about one _____

of coal.

12. Nuclear energy is generated from _____ .

13. Nuclear energy is considered to be a renewable resource.

True or False? (Circle one.)

Renewable Resources (p. 139)

14. What are renewable resources?

_____

_____

_____

_____

15. Solar energy can be used to run a calculator. Explain.

_____

_____

_____

_____

16. Electrical energy generated from falling water is called hydro-

gravity. True or False? (Circle one.)

17. A wind turbine changes the _____
energy of the air into electrical energy.

18. Geothermal energy results from the heating of Earth's

_____ .

19. Which of the following is NOT an example of biomass?

    a. plants   **c.** wood
    b. steel   **d.** waste

20. Corn can be used to make a cleaner-burning fuel for cars.

True or False? (Circle one.)

▲▲ CHAPTER 5

Chapter 5 Directed Reading, continued

The Two Sides to Energy Resources (p. 141)

Choose the energy resource in Column B that best matches the disadvantage in Column A, and write the corresponding letter in the space provided.

Column A	Column B
_____ **21.** requires large areas of farmland	**a.** fossil fuels
_____ **22.** produces radioactive waste	**b.** nuclear
_____ **23.** requires dams that disrupt river ecosystems	**c.** solar
_____ **24.** expensive for large-scale energy production	**d.** water
_____ **25.** waste water can damage soil	**e.** wind
_____ **26.** practical only in windy areas	**f.** geothermal
_____ **27.** burning produces smog and acid precipitation	**g.** biomass

Choose the energy resource in Column B that best matches the advantage in Column A, and write the corresponding letter in the space provided.

Column A	Column B
_____ **28.** power plants require little land	**a.** fossil fuels
_____ **29.** provides an almost limitless source of energy	**b.** nuclear
_____ **30.** easy to transport	**c.** solar
_____ **31.** is relatively inexpensive to generate	**d.** wind
_____ **32.** very concentrated forms of energy	**e.** geothermal

Section Review (p. 141)

Now that you've finished Section 4, review what you learned by answering the Section Review questions in your ScienceLog.

CHAPTER

6 DIRECTED READING WORKSHEET

Introduction to Electricity

As you read Chapter 6, which begins on page 150 of your textbook, answer the following questions.

It's Electrifying! (p. 150)

1. Why does the girl's hair stick out when she touches the Van de Graaf generator?

_____

_____

_____

_____

_____

_____

_____

Pre-Reading Questions (p. 150)

Answer these questions in your ScienceLog now. Then later, you'll have a chance to revise your answers based on what you've learned.

Start-Up Activity (p. 151)

2. What will you do in this activity?

_____

_____

_____

Section 1: Electric Charge and Static Electricity (p. 152)

3. When you shuffle your feet on the carpet on a dry day, you get a shock from the metal objects that you touch. What is the cause of this?

_____

_____

_____

Atoms and Charge (p. 152)

Choose the word in Column B that best matches the description in Column A, and write the corresponding letter in the space provided.

Column A	Column B
_____ **4.** composed of atoms	**a.** proton
_____ **5.** a positively charged particle of the nucleus	**b.** neutron
_____ **6.** a negatively charged particle found outside the nucleus	**c.** matter
_____ **7.** a particle of the nucleus that has no charge	**d.** electron

8. Why don't electrons fly out of atoms while traveling around the nucleus?

_____

_____

_____

9. According to the law of electric charges, like charges attract and

opposite charges repel. True or False? (Circle one.)

10. Which of the following does not determine the strength of an electric force between charged objects?

a. the age of the charges
b. the size of the charges
c. the distance between the charges
d. all of the above

11. The region around a charged object in which an electric force is

exerted on another charged object is called a(n) _____ .

Charge It! (p. 154)

Choose the word in Column B that best matches the definition in Column A, and write the corresponding letter in the space provided.

Column A	Column B
_____ **12.** "wiping" electrons from one object onto another	**a.** induction
_____ **13.** happens when electrons move from one object to another by direct contact	**b.** friction
_____ **14.** happens when charges in an uncharged object are rearranged without direct contact with a charged object	**c.** conduction

15. When objects are charged, no charges are created or destroyed.

True or False? (Circle one.)

16. An electroscope can determine which of the following?
   a. whether or not an object is charged
   b. the material that a charged object is made of
   c. the strength of the charge on an object
   d. how many electrons are involved in the charge

Mid-Section Review (p. 155)

Now that you've finished the first part of Section 1, review what you learned by answering the Mid-Section Review questions in your ScienceLog.

Moving Charges (p. 156)

17. Electric cords are often covered in plastic and have metal prongs.

This is because metal is a good _____ and

plastic is a good _____ .

18. Which of the following materials is NOT an insulator?
   a. rubber   **c.** air
   b. glass   **d.** mercury

Static Electricity (p. 156)

19. What is static electricity?
   a. an electric charge on a stationary object
   b. random electric signals from a radio
   c. the buildup of electric charges on an object
   d. electricity that moves away from an object

20. As charges move off an object, the object loses its static

electricity. This process is called _____ .

21. How does clothing that has become charged in a dryer lose its charge?

_____

_____

_____

_____

22. Electric discharges can happen quickly or slowly. True or False? (Circle one.)

23. Standing on a beach or golf course during a thunderstorm can be dangerous. Why?

_____

_____

_____

_____

24. An object that is _____ provides a path for electric charges to travel to the Earth.

Section Review (p. 158)

Now that you've finished Section 1, review what you learned by answering the Section Review questions in your ScienceLog.

Section 2: Electrical Energy (p. 159)

1. Name something that uses electrical energy and would be difficult for you to live without. Explain.

_____

_____

_____

_____

_____

Batteries Are Included (p. 159)

Choose the word in Column B that best matches the definition in Column A, and write the corresponding letter in the space provided.

Column A	Column B
_____ **2.** converts chemical energy into electrical energy	**a.** electrode
_____ **3.** have electrolytes that are solid or pastelike	**b.** battery
_____ **4.** mixture of chemicals that conducts electric current	**c.** electrolyte
_____ **5.** where charges enter or exit a cell	**d.** wet cell
_____ **6.** have liquid electrolytes	**e.** dry cell

Bring On the Potential (p. 160)

7. In a battery, electric current exists between the two electrodes because there is a difference in _____ between them.

8. If the potential difference of an electric current is increased, the current _____ .

Other Ways of Generating Electrical Energy (p. 161)

Choose the term in Column B that best matches the description in Column A, and write the corresponding letter in the space provided.

Column A	Column B
____ **9.** converts mechanical energy into electrical energy	**a.** silicon
____ **10.** converts light energy into electrical energy	**b.** copper
____ **11.** ejects electrons when struck by light	**c.** thermocouple
____ **12.** converts thermal energy into electrical energy	**d.** photocell
____ **13.** one type of wire used in some thermocouples	**e.** generator

Section Review (p. 161)

Now that you've finished Section 2, review what you learned by answering the Section Review questions in your ScienceLog.

Section 3: Electric Current (p. 162)

1. Where does most of the electrical energy you use every day come from?

  a. large rechargeable batteries
  b. electric power plants
  c. chemical reactions
  d. small generators

Current Revisited (p. 162)

2. The ampere is the unit of measure for current. True or False? (Circle one.)

3. In a wire, electrons travel at the speed of light. True or False? (Circle one.)

Label each of the following as a characteristic of alternating current or direct current. Write AC for alternating current or DC for direct current.

4. _____ It's produced by batteries and cells.

5. _____ It provides the electric current from outlets.

6. _____ The flow of charges continually change directions.

7. _____ Charges always flow in the same direction.

8. Another word for potential difference is _____,

which is expressed in _____ .

9. As voltage increases, the current decreases. True or False? (Circle one.)

10. The electrical outlets in the United States usually carry a

voltage of _____ V.

11. Look at the Biology Connection on page 163. Why do doctors intentionally create a high voltage across the chest of a heart-attack victim?

_____

_____

_____

_____

12. Opposition to the flow of electric charge is called

_____ .

13. Thin wires have _____ resistance than

thick wires do. Short wires have _____
resistance than long wires do.

14. An object's resistance depends on which of the following properties of the object? (Circle all that apply.)

    a. thickness
    b. length
    c. temperature
    d. color

Electric Power (p. 164)

15. Electric power is expressed in

    a. ohms.   **c.** amperes.
    b. volts.   **d.** watts.

16. Light bulbs may be labeled "100 W" or "60 W." This describes

  a. how long they burn.
  b. how they are disposed of.
  c. how fast the light travels.
  d. how bright they are.

17. One kilowatt is equal to _____ watts.

Measuring Electrical Energy (p. 165)

18. What do electric meters measure?

  a. power used
  b. voltage
  c. current
  d. electrical energy used

19. A television uses more power in one hour than a clothes

  dryer uses. True or False? (Circle one.)

Section Review (p. 165)

Now that you've finished Section 3, review what you learned by answering the Section Review questions in your ScienceLog.

Section 4: Electric Circuits (p. 166)

1. A complete _____ path through which electric charges flow is called a circuit.

Parts of a Circuit (p. 166)

2. An electric circuit always begins and ends in the same place.

  True or False? (Circle one.)

3. Which of the following are parts of all electric circuits? (Circle all that apply.)

  a. a load
  b. an energy source
  c. wires
  d. a switch

4. A(n) _____ opens and closes a circuit.

5. A(n) _____ is a device that was electrical energy to do work.

Types of Circuits (p. 167)

6. A _____ circuit is one in which all parts are connected in a single loop.

7. If one of the bulbs in Figure 19 on page 168 burned out, why would all of the lights go out?

_____

_____

_____

_____

_____

_____

_____

8. A _____ is one in which each load is placed on a separate branch.

9. If a load breaks in a parallel circuit, current will not run through the other branches. True or False? (Circle one.)

Household Circuits (p. 170)

10. Which of the following may cause a circuit failure? (Circle all that apply.)

    a. water   **c.** too many loads

    b. broken insulation   **d.** excess insulation

11. As more loads are added to a parallel circuit, the entire circuit draws more current. True or False? (Circle one.)

Circuit Safety (p. 171)

12. How does a fuse disrupt the flow of charges when the current is too high?

    a. A metal strip warms up and bends away from the circuit wires.

    b. A metal strip gets hot and melts.

    c. A metal strip changes from a conductor to an insulator.

    d. None of the above

13. A circuit breaker is a switch that automatically closes if the current in the circuit is too high. True or False? (Circle one.)

Section Review (p. 171)

Now that you've finished Section 4, review what you learned by answering the Section Review questions in your ScienceLog.

Name _____ Date _____ Class _____

DIRECTED READING WORKSHEET

Cells: The Basic Units of Living Things

As you read Chapter 7, which begins on page 182 of your textbook, answer the following questions.

Tiny Defenders (p. 182)

1. What are the "tiny defenders" in your body?

_____

_____

2. What happens to foreign bacteria cells that enter your body?

_____

_____

Pre-Reading Questions (p. 182)

Answer these questions in your ScienceLog now. Then later, you'll have a chance to revise your answers based on what you've learned.

Start-Up Activity (p. 183)

3. What type of cells are used in this activity?

    a. plant cells   **c.** dog cells

    b. frog cells   **d.** human cells

Section 1: Discovery and Diversity of Cells (p. 184)

4. Why weren't cells discovered until the mid-1600s?

_____

_____

_____

_____

The Discovery of Cells (p. 184)

5. What did Robert Hooke see when he looked at a thin slice of cork with his microscope?

_____

_____

6. *Cell* means _____ in Latin.

7. Did Hooke think that cells were found in all organisms? Explain.

_____

_____

_____

_____

Finding Cells in Other Organisms (p. 185)

8. Anton van Leeuwenhoek did NOT

  a. see bacteria.
  b. discover that frog and human blood cells are the same shape.
  c. discover that yeasts are single-celled organisms.
  d. see small organisms in pond scum.

9. Leeuwenhoek created the term *protists* for single-celled organisms.

True or False? (Circle one.)

The Cell Theory (p. 185)

10. When did scientists realize that all living things contain cells?

_____

_____

_____

_____

11. Rudolf Virchow saw that cells form only from

_____ cells.

12. The _____ is the basic unit of all living things.

Cells Are Small (p. 186)

13. Could a cell become large enough to cover New York City? Why or why not?

_____

_____

_____

_____

14. A chicken egg is one big cell. True or False? (Circle one.)

Parts of a Cell (p. 187)

Choose the cell feature in Column B that best matches the phrase in Column A, and write the corresponding letter in the space provided.

Column A	Column B
____ **15.** separates the cell's contents from its environment	**a.** cytoplasm
____ **16.** structures that enable cells to live and reproduce	**b.** cell membrane
____ **17.** the fluid inside a cell	**c.** DNA
____ **18.** controls the activities of a cell and contains the information needed to make new cells	**d.** organelles

Three Types of Cells (p. 66)

19. Bacteria are also called _____ .

Answer the following questions after reading pages 188–190. Mark each of the following statements *True* or *False*.

20. _____ Eubacteria are smaller than eukaryotic cells.

21. _____ Archaebacteria are more common than eubacteria.

22. _____ Eukaryotic cells are the smallest cells.

23. _____ Eukaryotic cells have a nucleus.

24. _____ Humans are eukaryotes.

Section Review (p. 190)

Now that you've finished Section 1, review what you learned by answering the Section Review questions in your ScienceLog.

Section 2: Eukaryotic Cells (p. 191)

1. Why do scientists need a microscope to look at eukaryotic cells?

_____

_____

_____

_____

Chapter 7 Directed Reading, continued

Cell Wall (p. 191)

2. Given that plants don't have bones, how do plants stand upright?

_____

_____

3. Some fungi have cell walls made of _____ ,
a material also found in the shells of insects.

Cell Membrane (p. 192)

4. What are the functions of the cell membrane?

_____

_____

_____

_____

_____

5. The cell membrane has two layers made of a kind of fat called

_____ .

The Cell's Scaffold (p. 193)

6. Which statement is NOT true of the cytoskeleton?
   a. It helps the cell keep its shape.
   b. It is made of one type of protein.
   c. It helps the cell move.
   d. It is located in the cytoplasm.

The Cell's Library (p. 193)

7. In a eukaryotic cell, the large organelle covered by two

membrane is the _____ .

8. The _____ is the dark spot inside the
nucleus that stores materials used to make ribosomes.

9. Why do you think the nucleus is called the cell's library?

_____

_____

_____

_____

Chapter 7 Directed Reading, continued

Protein Factories (p. 194)

10. Would cells die if they didn't have ribosomes? Explain.

_____

_____

_____

_____

11. Ribosomes are the largest organelles. True or False? (Circle one.)

The Cell's Delivery System (p. 194)

12. What are the functions of the endoplasmic reticulum?
(Circle all that apply.)

   a. It stores DNA.

   b. It makes lipids.

   c. It allows substances to move through it to different places in the cell.

   d. It breaks down chemicals that can damage the cell.

13. The membrane in rough ER is covered with _____ .

The Cell's Power Plants (p. 195)

14. Mitochondria "burn" sugar to release _____ .

15. Most ATP is produced in the outer membrane of mitochondria.

   True or False? (Circle one.)

Food Factories (p. 195)

16. Chloroplasts are organelles that make food in the cells of

_____ and _____ .

17. Chlorophyll traps the energy of sunlight and uses this energy to

make sugar in the process called _____ .

The Cell's Packaging Center (p. 196)

18. The Golgi complex ships proteins out of a

_____ .

19. The Golgi complex modifies carbohydrates. True or False?
(Circle one.)

Cell Compartments (p. 196)

20. How do vesicles form?

_____

_____

_____

_____

_____

_____

21. Lysosomes do NOT

    a. contain enzymes.   **c.** destroy damaged organelles.

    b. store liquids in the cell.   **d.** protect the cell from invaders.

22. Large vesicles that store water and other liquids in plant cells are

called _____ .

Eukaryotic Cells and Their Organelles (p. 198)

23. If you look at a cell with a microscope, how can you tell whether
it is a plant cell or an animal cell?

_____

_____

_____

_____

24. Look at the chart on page 199. What are the similarities and
differences in the organelles of fungi, protist 1, and protist 2 cells?

_____

_____

_____

_____

_____

_____

_____

Section Review (p. 199)

Now that you've finished Section 2, review what you learned by answering the Section Review questions in your ScienceLog.

Section 3: The Organization of Living Things (p. 200)

1. A single cell has all the items necessary to carry out

_____ .

2. In addition to being able to grow larger, what is another benefit of being multicellular?

_____

_____

_____

_____

_____

_____

3. A group of cells that work together to perform a specific job is

called a _____ .

4. What are three types of tissues found in plants?

_____

_____

_____

_____

5. An organ is made of a group of _____ .

6. A leaf is a plant organ. True or False? (Circle one.)

7. What is an organ system?

_____

_____

_____

_____

CHAPTER 7

8. What would happen if your digestive system stopped working?

_____

_____

_____

_____

Organisms (p. 203)

9. An _____ is anything that can live on its own.

10. Some organisms are made of a single cell. True or False? (Circle one.)

11. You are an example of a unicellular organism.

True or False? (Circle one.)

12. Multicellular organisms are composed of many different cells, tissues, organs, and organ systems. True or False? (Circle one.)

Structure and Function (p. 203)

13. _____ determines function in organisms.

14. Structure is the shape of a part and the material the part is

made of. True or False? (Circle one.)

15. The _____ of the part is the job the part does.

16. What is the function of the lungs and blood vessels?

_____

_____

_____

_____

Section Review (p. 203)

Now that you've finished Section 3, review what you learned by answering the Section Review questions in your ScienceLog.

Name _____ Date _____ Class _____

Population Changes and Heredity

As you read Chapter 8, which begins on page 212 of your textbook, answer the following questions.

Hidden Treasure (p. 212)

1. How many organisms do you see in the photograph?

_____

_____

_____

2. How do you think blennies' coloring makes some of them likely to live longer?

_____

_____

_____

Pre-Reading Questions (p. 212)

Answer these questions in your ScienceLog now. Then later, you'll have a chance to revise your answers based on what you've learned.

Start-Up Activity (p. 213)

3. What will you make in this activity?

_____

_____

Section 1: Change over Time (p. 214)

4. Scientists think Earth is about _____ years old.

Populations Change (p. 214)

5. A population is a group of the same kind of organism living in different places. True or False? (Circle one.)

6. The theory of _____ states that _____ characteristics in a population change over time.

Fossils (p. 215)

7. What is a fossil?

_____

_____

_____

_____

8. Fossils found in the upper layers of the Earth's crust are

_____ than fossils found in the lower

layers.

9. What is a mold? How is a fossil made from a mold?

_____

_____

_____

_____

_____

_____

The Fossil Record (p. 217)

10. What is the fossil record?

_____

_____

_____

11. The deeper in the Earth's crust fossils are found, the

_____ they tend to look like present day

organisms.

12. There are gaps in the fossil record because
   a. the conditions needed for fossils to form are rare.
   b. very few different organisms have lived on Earth.
   c. many fossils have been destroyed.
   d. not many people are looking for fossils.

Chapter 8 Directed Reading, continued

13. Why is the fossil record more complete for ocean life than for land-dwelling organisms?

_____

_____

_____

Comparing Organisms (p. 218)

14. Look at Figure 6. What similarities do you see between the cat leg, dolphin flipper, and bat wing?

_____

_____

_____

15. Similar structure with similar functions in different organisms always point to a common ancestor. True or False? (Circle one.)

Changing Characteristics (p. 219)

16. _____ are characteristics that help an organism survive and reproduce in its environment.

17. Look at Figure 10. How does being bright red help the strawberry dart-poison frog survive?

_____

_____

_____

Standing Out in the Crowd (p. 220)

18. No two dogs are exactly the same because not every individual has exactly the same _____ .

19. Because adaptations help an organism survive and reproduce, the individuals that are better adapted to their environment are _____ likely to pass their traits to future generations.

Section Review (p. 220)

Now that you've finished Section 1, review what you learned by answering the Section Review questions in your ScienceLog.

▲ ▲ ▲ CHAPTER 8

Section 2: How Do Populations Change? (p. 221)

1. What is one scientific discovery that occurred during the early 1800s?

_____

_____

_____

_____

_____

_____

_____

_____

_____

Charles Darwin (p. 158)

2. Darwin's father wanted Darwin to become a _____ ,

but Darwin earned a degree in _____

instead. However, Darwin was really interested in plants and animals.

Later, he served as the _____ on the HMS *Beagle*.

3. The Galápagos Islands are 965 km west of _____ ,
a country in South America.

4. Use Figure 13 to help you describe the beak of each of the finches
listed below. Explain how the adaptation helps each finch find food.

a. large ground finch

_____

_____

b. cactus finch

_____

_____

c. warbler finch

_____

_____

Darwin Does Some Thinking (p. 223)

5. Darwin's hypothesis was that the Galápagos finches were descendents of a population of finches that may have been blown from South America by a storm.

True or False? (Circle one.)

Answer these questions after reading pages 223–225. Column B lists some sources of ideas that Darwin used to develop his theory of evolution. Column A lists some of the ideas that contributed to the theory. Choose the appropriate source in Column B for the idea in Column A, and write the corresponding letter in the space provided. Sources can be used more than once.

Column A	Column B
____ **6.** Earth was much older than anyone had ever imagined.	**a.** farmers and breeders
____ **7.** Species produce more offspring than can survive.	**b.** geologists
____ **8.** Changes in animals and plants can happen in a few generations.	**c.** Thomas Malthus
____ **9.** Selective breeding produces individuals with certain desired traits.	
____ **10.** Hunger, sickness, and war keep human populations from expanding too rapidly.	

Natural Selection (p. 225)

11. Look at "Natural Selection in Four Steps" on page 226. What is the key to natural selection? Explain.

_____

_____

_____

_____

_____

_____

_____

_____

CHAPTER 8

Section Review (p. 226)

Now that you've finished Section 2, review what you learned by answering the Section Review questions in your ScienceLog.

Section 3: Natural Selection in Action (p. 227)

1. Sometimes bacteria are not killed by an antibiotic because they are

   naturally _____ to it.

Population Changes (p. 227)

2. Insects can quickly develop resistance to insecticides because they

   produce many _____ and have

   _____ generation times.

3. After the 1850s, _____ peppered moths became more common in certain areas because smoke from factories blackened tree trunks.

Forming a New Species (p. 229)

4. Two populations within a species are no longer considered the same species when

   a. they can no longer mate.
   b. they do not eat the same food.
   c. they do not look the same.
   d. they become physically separated.

5. After you read pages 229–230, place the following steps of speciation in the correct order by writing the appropriate number in the space provided.

   _____ The populations adapt to their environments.

   _____ The populations have different environments.

   _____ The populations become so different that they can no longer mate.

   _____ The populations become separated.

   _____ The populations are no longer the same species.

Section Review (p. 230)

Now that you've finished Section 3, review what you learned by answering the Section Review questions in your ScienceLog.

Section 4: Inheritance (p. 231)

1. Darwin observed that parents pass traits to their offspring, but he

   did not know how it happened. True or false. (Circle one.)

2. What organisms did Gregor Mendel study to work out his theory of inheritance?

_____

_____

Who Was Gregor Mendel? (p. 231)

3. Mendel studied heredity, the passing of traits from one

_____ to the next.

4. Mendel noticed that

    a. all of the parents' traits can be seen in their offspring.
    b. only plants have traits that don't appear in some generations.
    c. sometimes a trait will not appear in a generation.
    d. all traits appear in every generation.

5. For each characteristic, Mendel called the trait that appeared

_____ and the trait that seemed to

disappear _____ .

6. When Mendel allowed the first generation of pea plants to self-pollinate,

    a. all of the offspring had the recessive trait.
    b. some of the offspring had the recessive trait.
    c. none of the offspring had the recessive trait.
    d. the first-generation plants could not produce offspring.

Darwin and Mendel (p. 233)

7. Scientists used Mendel's principles of inheritance to understand

Darwin's ideas on _____ .

8. A change in an organism's hereditary information is called a

mutation. True or False? (Circle one.)

Mid-Section Review (p. 233)

Now that you've finished the first part of Section 4, review what you learned by answering the Mid-Section Review questions in your ScienceLog.

It's in Your Cells (p. 234)

9. The instructions for making proteins are given by parts of DNA

called _____ .

CHAPTER 8

10. Proteins determine which of the following traits?
(Circle all that apply.)

    a. straight hair   **c.** curly hair

    b. colors you see   **d.** height

11. Each gene spells out sequences of _____
for specific proteins.

Two Kinds of Reproduction (p. 235)

Mark each of the following statements *True* or *False*.

12. _____   Only one parent cell is needed for asexual
reproduction.

13. _____   Most single-celled organisms reproduce through
sexual reproduction.

14. _____   Each sex cell contains two copies of the genes for
every trait.

15. Why does sexual reproduction produce offspring who do not look
exactly like their parents?

_____

_____

_____

_____

_____

_____

_____

_____

_____

Section Review (p. 235)

Now that you've finished Section 4, review what you learned by
answering the Section Review questions in your ScienceLog.

CHAPTER

9 DIRECTED READING WORKSHEET

Senses and Responses of Living Things

As you read Chapter 9, which begins on page 244 of your textbook, answer the following questions.

Airborne Armadillos!! (p. 244)

1. Jumping is a _____ that occurs when an armadillo is frightened.

2. How does jumping straight up in the air help protect an armadillo?

_____

_____

_____

Pre-Reading Questions (p. 244)

Answer these questions in your ScienceLog now. Then later, you'll have a chance to revise your answers based on what you've learned.

Start-Up Activity (p. 245)

3. What will you do in this activity?

_____

_____

Section 1: Animals Sense (p. 246)

4. What happens in your body when you shiver?

_____

_____

5. When you are hungry, your body is detecting an external stimulus. True or False? (Circle one.)

Senses and Nerves (p. 246)

6. Special cells that detect internal and external stimuli are called sensory _____ .

7. Name some of the stimuli that animals have receptors for.

_____

_____

▲ ▲ CHAPTER 9

Chapter 9 Directed Reading, continued

8. Some flatworms have _____ , which are made up of light-absorbing pigments and nerves, and can determine the direction that light is coming from.

The Eyes Have It (p. 247)

9. Many insects have _____ eyes, which allow them to see images but differently than human eyes do.

Choose the part of the eye in Column B that best matches the functions in Column A, and write the corresponding letter in the space provided.

Column A	Column B
_____ **10.** focuses the light that enters the eye	**a.** pupil
_____ **11.** clear membrane that protects the eye	**b.** lens
_____ **12.** opening that allows light to enter the eye	**c.** retina
_____ **13.** carries impulses from the back of the eye to the brain	**d.** cornea
_____ **14.** layer with receptors that lines the back of the eye	**e.** optic nerve

Sounds Good to Me (p. 248)

15. Put the following statements in the proper sequence to explain how we hear. Write the appropriate number in the space provided.

_____ One of the tiny ear bones vibrates against the fluid-filled cochlea in the inner ear.

_____ Inside the cochlea, vibrations cause waves.

_____ Sound waves are directed through the outer ear into the middle ear.

_____ Sound receptors change waves to nerve impulses and send them to the brain.

_____ The eardrum makes tiny bones vibrate.

16. Crickets, as well as some other types of insects, use receptors on

their _____ to pick up sounds.

Getting Nosy (p. 249)

17. In humans, olfactory cells are receptors that are located in the

nasal cavity. True or False? (Circle one.)

18. Male silkworms have olfactory cells on their

_____ .

Chapter 9 Directed Reading, continued

19. Why is it difficult to taste food when you have a stuffy nose?

_____

_____

_____

_____

_____

_____

_____

A Matter of Taste (p. 250)

20. In humans, taste receptors are located on _____,

on the tongue.

21. The four tastes that are detected by the taste receptors are salty, sweet,

_____ , and _____ .

How Touching (p. 251)

22. What mixture of stimuli affects the sense of touch in humans?

_____

_____

_____

_____

23. Octopuses can find a meal just by _____
for it with their tentacles.

Section Review (p. 251)

Now that you've finished Section 1, review what you learned by answering the Section Review questions in your ScienceLog.

Section 2: Animals Respond (p. 252)

1. Which of the following are survival responses of animals? (Circle all that apply.)

   a. finding food

   b. finding a place to live

   c. avoiding being eaten

   d. finding water

▲ ▲ ▲
▲ **CHAPTER 9**

Responding to Internal Stimuli (p. 252)

2. How does your body remind you to drink water?

_____

_____

_____

3. When you are hungry, your brain is telling you that your cells

need _____ .

4. Why don't you have to remember to breathe when you sleep?

_____

_____

_____

5. Which of the following functions is NOT controlled by hormones?

   a. human growth
   b. breathing
   c. signaling changes during puberty
   d. releasing sugar stored in your liver

6. Treehoppers go through several big changes in their lives which

are responses to internal stimuli. True or False? (Circle one.)

Responding to External Stimuli (p. 254)

7. External stimuli come from _____ the
body.

8. A _____ is an animal that eats another
animal. The animal that gets eaten is called

_____ .

9. Explain how bats use echolocation to find food.

_____

_____

_____

_____

_____

_____

Match each animal in Column B to its response to a predator in Column A, and write the corresponding letter in the space provided.

Column A	Column B
____ **10.** stands guard and attacks if the predator gets too close	**a.** rabbit
____ **11.** freezes so it won't be noticed	**b.** octopus
____ **12.** changes its skin color to blend in with its environment	**c.** wasp

13. Which of the following does NOT involve animal communication?

   a. marking a territory
   b. finding a family member or a mate
   c. scaring off predators
   d. detecting changes in Earth's magnetic field

Responding to Seasonal Changes (p. 256)

14. An internal control of a natural cycle is called a biological clock.

   True or False? (Circle one.)

15. Many animals _____ when winter approaches because food is scarce.

16. Look at the Astronomy Connection on p. 256. What happens when the Northern Hemisphere is tilted toward the sun?

_____

_____

_____

_____

17. What happens to an animal's body when it hibernates?

_____

_____

_____

18. _____ is a period of reduced activity in the summer.

Section Review (p. 257)

Now that you've finished Section 2, review what you learned by answering the Section Review questions in your ScienceLog.

▲ ▲ ▲ **CHAPTER 9**

Section 3: Plants Sense and Respond (p. 258)

1. Plants never respond to stimuli. True or False? (Circle one.)

Plants Respond to External Stimuli (p. 258)

2. Plant growth away from a stimulus is a _____ tropism.

3. Plant growth _____ a stimulus is a positive tropism.

Answer these questions after reading pp. 258–259. Mark each of the following statements T for thigmotropism, P for phototropism, or G for gravitropism.

4. _____ a plant's shoot tips grow upward

5. _____ a plant grows toward light

6. _____ tendrils hold onto other things

7. _____ a plant's root tips grow downward

8. _____ a vine coils around a twig

Plants Respond to Seasonal Changes (p. 260)

9. Short-day plants make flowers
   a. when night length is shorter
   b. when day length is longer
   c. only in spring or early summer
   d. only in late summer or early autumn

10. How does losing leaves help a tree survive?

_____

_____

_____

_____

11. What happens to leaves as the chlorophyll in them breaks down?

_____

_____

_____

Section Review (p 261)

Now that you've finished Section 3, review what you learned by answering the Section Review questions in your ScienceLog.

CHAPTER

10 DIRECTED READING WORKSHEET

Connections in the Environment

As you read Chapter 10, which begins on page 270 of your textbook, answer the following questions.

Midnight Snack (p. 270)

1. How are the bat and centipede connected?

_____

_____

2. Look up the word "pallid" in the dictionary. Why do you think the bat shown is called a "pallid bat"?

_____

_____

Pre-Reading Questions (p. 270)

Answer these questions in your ScienceLog now. Then later, you'll have a chance to revise your answers based on what you've learned.

Start-Up Activity (p. 271)

3. What is the purpose of this activity?

_____

_____

_____

Section 1: Life in the Environment (p. 272)

4. The study of the relationships between _____

and their _____ is called ecology.

How the Environment Works (p. 272)

5. Name three living parts and one nonliving part of the environment shown in Figure 1.

_____

_____

_____

▲▲ **CHAPTER 10** ▲

6. Number the five levels of the environment in order from smallest to largest. Write the appropriate number in the space provided.

_____ ecosystem

_____ biosphere

_____ community

_____ organism

_____ population

Responding to the Nonliving Environment (p. 274)

7. Which of the following are part of the nonliving environment? (Circle all that apply.)

a. water

b. wind

c. air temperature

d. sunlight

8. Give two examples of ways that animals respond to air temperature.

_____

_____

_____

_____

_____

_____

Responding to the Living Environment (p. 276)

9. Why do badgers dig dens?

_____

_____

10. Which of the following is NOT an example of an organism reacting to other organisms?

a. Your stomach growls, so you eat to stop your hunger.

b. A caterpillar puffs up its back to look like a snake.

c. A bacterium in your body gets a food supply from you and responds by making a vitamin your body needs.

d. A spider tries to catch a fly.

Section Review (p. 277)

Now that you've finished Section 1, review what you learned by answering the Section Review questions in your ScienceLog.

Section 2: Living Things Need Energy (p. 278)

1. Which of the following living things need energy to survive? (Circle all that apply.)

   a. prairie dogs   **c.** coyotes
   b. plants   **d.** bacteria

The Energy Connection (p. 278)

2. Producers use energy from the _____ to

   make food through a process called _____ .

3. _____ are the main producers in the ocean.

4. Consumers get energy from eating _____ or other organisms.

Choose the type of consumer in Column B that best matches the phrase in Column A, and write the corresponding letter in the space provided.

Column A	Column B
_____ **5.** feeds on the bodies of dead animals	**a.** herbivore
_____ **6.** eats animals	**b.** carnivore
_____ **7.** eats plants	**c.** omnivore
_____ **8.** eats both plants and animals	**d.** scavenger

9. Which of the following organisms are decomposers? (Circle all that apply.)

   a. bacteria   **c.** turkey vultures
   b. catfish   **d.** fungi

Food Chains and Food Webs (p. 280)

10. A food chain is the path of _____ from one feeding level to another in an ecosystem.

11. The energy flow in a food chain begins with a plant using

    _____ energy from the

    _____ to make food for itself.

12. Look at the food web in Figure 7. Which animals eat the squirrel?

    _____

    _____

    _____

CHAPTER 10

Energy Pyramids (p. 282)

13. Look at the energy pyramid on page 282. Why does there have to be more grass than prairie dogs in the community?

_____

_____

_____

_____

_____

14. As you go up the energy pyramid, the number of organisms at

each level _____ .

The Gray Wolf, A Case Study (p. 283)

15. Why were gray wolves put back in Yellowstone Park?

_____

_____

_____

_____

16. Why are ranchers near Yellowstone not happy about the return of wolves to the National Park?

_____

_____

_____

_____

Section Review (p. 283)

Now that you've finished Section 2, review what you learned by answering the Section Review questions in your ScienceLog.

CHAPTER

11 DIRECTED READING WORKSHEET

Classification of Living Things

As you read Chapter 11, which begins on page 292 of your textbook, answer the following questions.

A Name Game (p. 292)

1. How would you name a new insect you had found?

_____

_____

_____

_____

_____

Pre-Reading Questions (p. 292)

Answer these questions in your ScienceLog now. Then later, you'll have a chance to revise your answers based on what you've learned.

Start-Up Activity (p. 293)

2. What are three shoe features you would include in your table?

_____

_____

_____

Section 1: Classification: Sorting It All Out (p. 294)

3. Classifying plants based on whether or not they are safe to eat is

an example of classification. True or False? (Circle one.)

Why Classify? (p. 294)

4. Why do biologists classify organisms? (Circle all that apply.)
   a. to make sense of the large number of living things
   b. to discover how many known species there are
   c. to study the characteristics of known species
   d. to study the relationships between species

What Is the Basis for Classification? (p. 295)

5. Carolus Linnaeus founded taxonomy, which is the science of

studying the past. True or False? (Circle one.)

Choose the characteristics in Column B that best match the group of animals in Column A, and write the corresponding letter in the space provided.

Column A	Column B
____ **6.** the brown bear, lion, and house cat	**a.** hair, mammary glands
____ **7.** the house cat, lion, brown bear, and platypus	**b.** give birth to live young
____ **8.** the house cat and lion	**c.** retractable claws

Levels of Classification (p. 296)

9. What are the seven levels of classification?

_____

_____

_____

10. Look at Figure 4. Why do you think the bird is included in phylum Chordata but not in class Mammalia?

_____

_____

_____

_____

11. In the scientific name for the Indian elephant, *Elephas maximus,*

Elephas is the _____ and *maximus* is the

_____ . *Elephas maximus* can be abbreviated

_____ .

Dichotomous Keys (p. 298)

12. Look at the dichotomous key on page 299. What type of animal does not fly and has a long naked tail that is not flat?

_____

_____

Section Review (p. 299)

Now that you've finished Section 1, review what you learned by answering the Section Review questions in your ScienceLog.

Section 2: The Six Kingdoms (p. 300)

1. Before the discovery of organisms like Euglena, the only kingdoms

   used to classify organisms were _____ and

   _____ .

What Is It? (p. 300)

2. What are the characteristics of Euglena? (Circle all that apply.)

   a. It can move from place to place.
   b. It is multicellular.
   c. It can make its own food.
   d. It can get food from other living things.

3. Scientists classify Euglena in kingdom _____ .

4. Do you think there will always be six kingdoms used for
   classifying organisms? Explain.

   _____

   _____

   _____

   _____

The Two Kingdoms of Bacteria (p. 301)

5. Bacteria are different from all other living things in that

   a. they are single-celled organisms.
   b. they have ribosomes.
   c. they do not have a nucleus.
   d. they are microscopic.

Choose the bacteria kingdom in Column B that best matches the
description in Column A, and write the corresponding letter in the
space provided. The bacteria kingdoms may be used more than once.

Column A	Column B
_____ **6.** live inside the human body	**a.** Archaebacteria
_____ **7.** cause pneumonia	**b.** Eubacteria
_____ **8.** live in places where most living things could not survive	
_____ **9.** part of the name comes from a Greek word meaning "ancient"	
_____ **10.** changes milk to yogurt	

Chapter 11 Directed Reading, continued

Kingdom Protista (p. 302)

11. Kingdom Protista includes all eukaryotes that are not

_____ , _____ ,

or _____ .

12. All protists are single-celled organisms.

True or False? (Circle one.)

Kingdom Plantae (p. 303)

13. Plants make sugar by using energy from the

_____ in a process called

_____ .

14. All plants have many cells. True or False? (Circle one.)

Kingdom Fungi (p. 304)

15. List two examples of fungi.

_____

_____

16. Fungi absorb nutrients from their surroundings
   a. through photosynthesis.
   b. after breaking down matter using digestive juices.
   c. by surrounding their food and engulfing it.
   d. by eating like animals.

Kingdom Animalia (p. 305)

17. Most animals share which of the following characteristics?
   (Circle all that apply.)
   a. They have a nervous system.
   b. They can move about.
   c. They carry out photosynthesis.
   d. They are unicellular.

18. Unlike the cells of fungi, plants, most protists, and bacteria,

   animal cells do not have a _____ .

Section Review (p. 305)

Now that you've finished Section 2, review what you learned by
answering the Section Review questions in your ScienceLog.

CHAPTER

12   DIRECTED READING WORKSHEET

Invertebrates

As you read Chapter 12, which begins on page 316 of your textbook, answer the following questions.

A Sci-Fi Slug? (p. 317)

1. What does food have to do with the sea slugs' bright coloring?

_____

_____

_____

2. Sea slugs and all the other animals in this chapter do not have a

_____ .

Pre-Reading Questions (p. 316)

Answer these questions in your ScienceLog now. Then later, you'll have a chance to revise your answers based on what you've learned.

Start-Up Activity (p.317)

3. What is the purpose of this activity?

_____

_____

_____

_____

Section 1: Simple Invertebrates (p. 318)

4. _____ 1 million invertebrates have been discovered and named.

5. Invertebrates make up about _____ percent of all animal species.

No Backbones Here! (p. 318)

In the space provided, write B if the animal has bilateral symmetry, R if the animal has radial symmetry, or A if the animal has asymmetry.

6. _____ sea star

7. _____ ant

8. _____ sponge

CHAPTER 12

Sponges (p. 319)

9. Is a sponge considered an animal? Explain.

_____

_____

_____

_____

10. Describe how a sponge gets its food from the water.

_____

_____

_____

_____

_____

_____

_____

_____

Cnidarians (p. 320)

11. Which of the following is true about cnidarians?
(Circle all that apply.)

  a. They have tentacles covered with stinging cells.
  b. They have radial symmetry.
  c. They live only in salt water.
  d. They include sponges, corals, and hydras.

12. Cnidarians digest food in their gut. True or False? (Circle one.)

13. Corals live on rocky, underwater structures called

  _____ .

Flatworms (p. 321)

14. Which of the following does NOT describe flatworms?

  a. They have a head.
  b. They have radial symmetry.
  c. They have eyespots.
  d. They have sensory lobes.

15. Planarians use sensory lobes to find food by

    a. sight.

    b. touch.

    c. taste.

    d. smell.

16. A living thing that feeds on another living thing is called a

_____ .

17. Tapeworms often live outside a host. True or False?
(Circle one.)

18. Tapeworms have no _____

or _____ on their heads.

Roundworms (p. 321)

19. Describe the body of a typical roundworm.

_____

_____

20. All roundworms are parasites. True or False? (Circle one.)

Section Review (p. 321)

Now that you've finished Section 1, review what you learned by
answering the Section Review questions in your ScienceLog.

Section 2: Mollusks and Annelid Worms (p. 322)

1. What is one feature of mollusks and annelid worms that make
them more complex organisms than roundworms, flatworms,
sponges, and cnidarians?

_____

_____

_____

_____

Mollusks (p. 322)

2. Which of the three classes of mollusks includes slugs and snails?

_____

_____

3. Snails and slugs use a _____ to scrape algae off rocks.

4. How are open and closed circulatory systems different?

   a. Open circulatory systems have sinuses.
   b. Closed circulatory systems have sinuses.
   c. Only open circulatory systems have blood vessels.
   d. Only closed circulatory systems have blood vessels.

5. Octopuses and squids have the most advanced

   _____ system of all invertebrates, and

they have a large _____ .

Choose the part of the mollusk in Column B that best matches the definition in Column A, and write the corresponding letter in the space provided.

Column A	Column B
_____ **6.** a layer of tissue that protects the bodies of mollusks that do not have a shell	**a.** shell
_____ **7.** formed by the gills, gut, and other organs	**b.** mantle
_____ **8.** keeps land mollusks from drying out	**c.** foot
_____ **9.** helps the mollusk move	**d.** visceral mass

Annelid Worms (p. 324)

10. The head, tail, and all other segments of an earthworm are identical.

True or False? (Circle one.)

11. How do earthworms help improve soil? (Circle all that apply.)

   a. They eat bugs that poison the soil.
   b. Their wastes make soil richer for plants to grow in.
   c. They dig tunnels that allow air and water to reach deep into the soil.
   d. They have bristles that protect plant roots.

12. What does the bristle worm in Figure 9 use its bristles to do?

   a. burrow   **c.** avoid predators
   b. feed by filtering particles from the water   **d.** protect itself from drying out

13. Some leeches are parasites, some are scavengers, and some are

predators. True or False? (Circle one.)

14. How are leeches used by doctors?

_____

_____

_____

_____

_____

_____

Section Review (p.325)

Now that you've finished Section 2, review what you learned by answering the Section Review questions in your ScienceLog.

Section 3: Arthropods (p. 326)

1. Which of the following invertebrates is NOT an arthropod?

   a. a crab   **c.** a centipede

   b. a spider   **d.** a sea urchin

Characteristics of Arthropods (p. 326)

2. All arthropods have a segmented body with specialized parts.

   True or False? (Circle one.)

3. How do jointed limbs help an arthropod?

_____

_____

4. Arthropods have a hard _____ that is

   made of _____ and a special substance called

   _____ .

5. How does a tarantula use its bristles?

_____

_____

_____

_____

6. Most arthropods have _____ eyes made of
many identical, light-sensitive units.

Chapter 12 Directed Reading, continued

Kinds of Arthropods (p. 328)

7. Millipedes have _____ pair(s) of legs on each

segment, while centipedes have _____ pair(s).

8. All crustaceans have _____ and two pairs

of _____ .

9. Ticks and mites are types of insects. True or False? (Circle one.)

The World of Insects (p. 330)

10. Where is the only place on Earth where insects do not live?

_____

11. Why are insects important to us?

_____

_____

12. Name one way in which insects are pests?

_____

_____

_____

_____

_____

_____

Read pages 329–330 before answering questions 13–18. Match each
type of arthropod in Column B to the correct statement in Column
A, and write the corresponding letter in the appropriate space.
Arthropod types can be used more than once.

Column A	Column B
____ **13.** has a cephalothorax	**a.** arachnid
____ **14.** has two main body parts	**b.** insect
____ **15.** has three main body parts	
____ **16.** has antennae	
____ **17.** has mandibles	
____ **18.** has chelicerae	

Look at Figure 21 on page 331. Place the following stages of complete metamorphosis in order by writing the appropriate number in the space provided.

19. _____ pupa

20. _____ larva

21. _____ egg

22. _____ adult

Section Review (p. 331)

Now that you've finished Section 3, review what you learned by answering the Section Review questions in your ScienceLog.

Section 4: Echinoderms (p. 332)

1. If you went snorkeling in a freshwater lake, would you see any echinoderms? Why or why not?

_____

_____

_____

_____

Spiny Skinned (p. 332)

2. Echinoderms have spiny skin. True or False? (Circle one.)

3. Some echinoderms have a hard, bony _____.

Bilateral or Radial? (p. 332)

4. Most echinoderms start out with _____

symmetry and later develop _____ symmetry.

The Nervous System (p. 333)

5. A sea star has a circle of nerve fibers around its

_____ called a nerve ring.

6. Which of the following can a sea star sense? (Circle all that apply.)

    a. smell   **c.** sound

    b. light   **d.** taste

Water Vascular System (p. 333)

7. Which of the following is NOT part of the water vascular system?

a. ampulla   **c.** sieve plate
b. radial canals   **d.** radial nerve

8. Tube feet help a sea star to move and to capture food.

True or False? (Circle one.)

Kinds of Echinoderms (p. 334)

9. Besides using their tube feet, how else do some sea urchins move from place to place?

_____

_____

_____

10. Which of the following invertebrates is NOT an echinoderm?

a. barnacle
b. brittle star
c. feather star
d. sea cucumber

11. Sea lilies and feather stars may have _____ feathery arms.

12. What do sea stars, brittle stars, basket stars, and feather stars have in common?

_____

_____

_____

_____

Section Review (p. 335)

Now that you've finished Section 4, review what you learned by answering the Section Review questions in your ScienceLog.

CHAPTER

13 DIRECTED READING WORKSHEET

Fishes, Amphibians, and Reptiles

As you read Chapter 13, which begins on page 344 of your textbook, answer the following questions.

A Blast From the Past! (p. 345)

1. What was so amazing about Marjorie Courtenay Latimer's discovery?

_____

_____

_____

Pre-Reading Questions (p. 344)

Answer these questions in your ScienceLog now. Then later, you'll have a chance to revise your answers based on what you've learned.

Start-Up Activity (p. 345)

2. What will building a model of an oily liver teach you about sharks?

_____

_____

_____

Section 1: What Are Vertebrates? (p. 346)

3. What does a dinosaur skeleton have in common with your skeleton?

_____

_____

_____

Vertebrates Are Chordates (p. 346)

Mark each of the following statements *True* or *False*.

4. _____ Vertebrates make up the largest group of chordates.

5. _____ Lancelets do not have a backbone and therefore are not true chordates.

6. _____ An organism must have all four of the special chordate body parts as an adult in order to be considered a chordate.

CHAPTER 13

Use Figure 2 on page 347 to choose the term in Column B that best matches the definition in Column A. Then write the corresponding letter in the space provided.

Column A	Column B
____ **7.** This structure is full of fluid.	**a.** notochord
____ **8.** This structure begins behind the anus.	**b.** pharyngeal pouches
____ **9.** In most vertebrates, this structure disappears and a backbone grows in its place.	**c.** tail
____ **10.** These develop into gills or other body parts as an embryo matures.	**d.** hollow nerve cord

Getting a Backbone (p. 347)

11. Vertebrates are different from other chordates because

    a. tunicates and lancelets have pharyngeal pouches.
    b. they have a notochord.
    c. they do not have a tail.
    d. they have a backbone and a skull.

12. A column of bones called _____ protects

the spinal cord, and a _____ protects the head.

13. Cartilage forms the flexible parts of your ears and nose.

True or False? (Circle one.)

Are Vertebrates Warm or Cold? (p. 348)

14. The chemical changes that take place in an animal's body

cells happen only at certain temperatures. True or False? (Circle one.)

15. An endotherm's body temperature _____ when the temperature of the environment changes.

16. How does an endotherm stay warm when it's cold outside?

_____

_____

_____

_____

17. Which of the following statements is NOT true?

    a. Ectotherms include most fish, amphibians, and reptiles.

    b. Ectotherms' body temperature does not change.

    c. Ectotherms' body temperature changes with the temperature of their environment.

    d. Ectotherms are sometimes called "coldblooded."

Section Review (p. 348)

Now that you've finished Section 1, review what you learned by answering the Section Review questions in your ScienceLog.

Section 2: Fishes (p. 349)

1. Which of the following statements is NOT true?

    a. Fish can live only in the ocean.

    b. Fish appeared on Earth about 500 million years ago.

    c. There are more species of fishes today than all other vertebrates combined.

    d. There are more than 25,000 species of fishes.

Fish Characteristics (p. 349)

2. What characteristics do fishes need in order to actively search for food?

_____

_____

_____

_____

_____

3. What structures help fish move, steer, stop, and balance?

_____

_____

4. Which of the following are functions of scales? (Circle all that apply.)

    a. protecting the fish's body

    b. sensing water vibrations

    c. lowering the friction as the fish swims

    d. helping the fish breathe

5. The lateral line system in a fish enables it to keep track of

information. True or False? (Circle one.)

CHAPTER 13

6. How do fish use their gills to breathe?

_____

_____

_____

_____

_____

_____

7. In external fertilization, the male fish drops sperm on the unfertilized eggs in the water. True or False? (Circle one.)

8. After internal fertilization takes place, fish always give birth to live young. True or False? (Circle one.)

Kinds of Fishes (p. 351)

9. There are _____ different classes of fishes living today. Two other classes of fishes are now

_____ .

10. Which is NOT true of jawless fishes?
 a. They are eel-like.
 b. They have a backbone.
 c. They have a round mouth.
 d. They have a skull, a brain, and eyes.

11. The skeleton of a cartilaginous fish, such as a ray, never changes from cartilage to bone. True or False? (Circle one.)

12. Cartilaginous fishes have fully functional

_____ .

13. Look at the Brain Food on page 352. How can a shark's skin hurt you?

_____

_____

_____

_____

14. Which of the following are ways that cartilaginous fishes keep from suffocating? (Circle all that apply.)

   a. They keep swimming.
   b. They go to the surface for air.
   c. They pump water across their gills.
   d. They swim at certain depths.

15. Lungfishes like the one shown in Figure 9 on page 353 can gulp air.

   True or False? (Circle one.)

16. Bony fishes have a _____ made of bone, not cartilage.

17. The body of a bony fish is covered by scales. True or False? (Circle one.)

18. Which is NOT true of a swim bladder?

   a. It's found in bony fishes.
   b. It's filled with oxygen and other gases from the bloodstream.
   c. It helps fishes float in one place without swimming.
   d. It helps fishes steer against wave action.

Section Review (p. 353)

Now that you've finished Section 2, review what you learned by answering the Section Review questions in your ScienceLog.

Section 3: Amphibians (p. 354)

1. What made the land such a wonderful place for vertebrates 350 million years ago?

   _____

   _____

Moving to Land (p. 354)

2. Most amphibians get oxygen from the air through their

   _____ .

3. How were early amphibians different from amphibians today?

   _____

   _____

   _____

   _____

4. Early amphibians needed to return to the water to keep from drying out, to keep from overheating, and to lay their eggs.

   True or False? (Circle one.)

CHAPTER 13

Characteristics of Amphibians (p. 355)

5. Amphibian embryos must develop in a very wet environment because

    a. their eggs do not have a shell or membrane to stop water loss.

    b. they begin life as fish.

    c. they are ectotherms.

    d. the water is less polluted than the air.

6. How do amphibians lead a "double-life"?

_____

_____

_____

_____

_____

Mark each of the following statements *True* or *False*.

7. _____ Amphibians do not drink water.

8. _____ An amphibian's thin skin makes it easy for the animal to become dehydrated.

9. _____ Some amphibians breathe only through their skin.

10. _____ All amphibians with brightly colored skin are deadly.

11. When an amphibian goes through _____ , it changes from its immature form, a tadpole, into its adult form.

12. Where does the embryo of the Darwin frog finish developing?

_____

_____

_____

Kinds of Amphibians (p. 357)

13. Frogs and toads belong to the same group of amphibians.

True or False? (Circle one.)

14. How are caecilians different from most other amphibians? (Circle all that apply.)

    a. They don't have legs.

    b. Some have bony scales.

    c. They are shaped like worms or snakes.

    d. They have thin, moist skin.

15. How are salamanders similar to their prehistoric amphibian ancestors?

_____

_____

16. A good place to look for a salamander in North America is under a

_____ or a _____ .

17. All salamanders go through metamorphosis. True or False? (Circle one.)

18. Frogs and toads are found only in temperate parts of the world.

True or False? (Circle one.)

Use the information on page 358 to mark each of the following phrases F if it is characteristic of a frog, T if it is characteristic of a toad, or B if it is characteristic of both a frog and a toad.

19. _____ extendible, sticky tongue

20. _____ dry, bumpy skin

21. _____ spends more time in water

22. _____ vocal chords

23. _____ powerful leg muscles

24. _____ well-developed ears

25. _____ smooth, moist skin

26. Frogs have a special structure called a vocal sac that humans don't have. What does this structure do?

_____

_____

_____

_____

_____

_____

Section Review (p. 358)

Now that you've finished Section 3, review what you learned by answering the Section Review questions in your ScienceLog.

Section 4: Reptiles (p. 359)

1. Which of the following traits allow reptiles to live completely out of the water? (Circle all that apply.)

    a. an egg that can be laid on dry land
    b. strong legs
    c. thick, dry skin
    d. teeth

Characteristics of Reptiles (p. 360)

2. Reptiles never use lungs to breathe. True or False? (Circle one.)

3. How is a reptile's skin an important adaptation for life on land?

    _____

    _____

    _____

    _____

4. Reptiles are less active when the environment is

    _____ and more active when the

    environment is _____ .

5. Most reptiles live in mild climates because they cannot handle the cold polar regions. True or False? (Circle one.)

6. What are some of the advantages of an amniotic egg and its parts?

    _____

    _____

    _____

    _____

    _____

    _____

    _____

    _____

    _____

ame _____ Date _____ Class _____

hapter 13 Directed Reading, continued

Choose the part of the amniotic egg in Column B that best matches the definition in Column A, and write the corresponding letter in the space provided.

Column A	Column B
_____ **7.** gives the embryo a rich supply of food	**a.** yolk
_____ **8.** stores the embryo's wastes and passes it oxygen	**b.** albumen
_____ **9.** keeps the egg from drying out	**c.** amniotic sac
_____ **10.** fluid-filled structure that protects the embryo	**d.** allantois
_____ **11.** provides the embryo with water and protein	**e.** shell

12. Which of the following are true of reptiles? (Circle all that apply.)

    a. Reptiles don't go through metamorphosis.

    b. Reptile embryos develop directly into tiny young reptiles.

    c. All reptiles lay eggs.

    d. Reptiles don't reproduce by external fertilization.

Kinds of Reptiles (p. 361)

13. The number of reptile species living today is _____ the number that lived in the age of the dinosaurs.

14. List the three groups of modern reptiles.

_____

_____

_____

15. Which of the following is NOT true of both turtles and tortoises?

    a. They are only distantly related to the other reptiles.

    b. They spend all of their lives on land.

    c. Their armorlike shells protect them from predators.

    d. They are slow and inflexible.

16. All crocodiles and alligators eat _____ .

17. What is an advantage that crocodiles and alligators have over their prey?

_____

_____

_____

HAPTER 13

opyright © by Holt, Rinehart and Winston. All rights reserved.

XAS EDITION, GRADE 6, UNIT 4 RESOURCES **95**

18. Look at Figure 23 on page 362. How can you tell the difference between a crocodile and an alligator?

_____

_____

_____

_____

Mark each of the following statements *True* or *False*.

19. _____ Most lizards are more than 30 cm long.

20. _____ Lizards may live in the ocean.

21. _____ Snakes are carnivores.

22. _____ Some snakes squeeze and suffocate their prey.

23. _____ Snakes flick their tongues in the air to scare predators.

24. _____ Snakes see and hear very well.

25. How does a snake use its tongue to smell?

_____

_____

_____

_____

_____

_____

_____

_____

_____

Section Review (p. 363)

Now that you've finished Section 4, review what you've learned by answering the Section Review questions in your ScienceLog.

Birds and Mammals

As you read Chapter 14, which begins on page 372 of your textbook, answer the following questions.

Pest Control for Giraffes! (p. 372)

1. How can this bird provide pest control for giraffes?

_____

_____

Pre-Reading Questions (p. 372)

Answer these questions in your ScienceLog now. Then later, you'll have a chance to revise your answers based on what you've learned.

Start-Up Activity (p. 373)

2. What is the purpose of this experiment?

_____

_____

Section 1: Characteristics of Birds (p. 374)

3. Which of the following characteristics do birds share with modern-day reptiles? (Circle all that apply.)

   a. Birds have thick, dry scales on their legs and feet.
   b. Birds are vertebrates.
   c. Birds lay amniotic eggs.
   d. Birds lay eggs with shells.

4. Name two characteristics that set birds apart from other animals.

_____

_____

_____

_____

5. Unlike most reptiles, fishes, and amphibians, birds maintain a

_____ .

Birds of a Feather (p. 374)

5. When bird feathers wear out, birds shed their worn feathers and grow new ones. True or False? (Circle one.)

6. Down feathers help keep birds from losing _____ .

7. The main function of contour feathers is to
  a. form a streamlined surface.
  b. form a rough surface.
  c. provide protection.
  d. provide warmth.

8. How does preening make a bird's feathers water-repellent?

_____

_____

_____

_____

High-Energy Animals (p. 375)

9. How do birds cool off on hot days?
  a. They fly higher in the atmosphere, where the air is cooler.
  b. They lay their feathers flat and pant like dogs do.
  c. They shed feathers.
  d. They sweat.

Eat Like a Bird (p. 375)

10. Birds eat a lot of food because they require a lot of energy.
  True or False? (Circle one.)

11. What type of food do birds eat?

_____

_____

_____

12. How does a gizzard help a bird digest food?

_____

_____

_____

_____

Up, Up, and Away (p. 376)

Choose the bird characteristic in Column B that best matches the use in Column A, and write the corresponding letter in the space provided.

Column A	Column B
_____ **13.** pumps a fast, steady stream of oxygen-rich blood to the flight muscles	**a.** large eyes
_____ **14.** allows a bird to quickly turn, drop, and pull up	**b.** air sac
_____ **15.** help birds see food from a distance	**c.** short, rounded wings
_____ **16.** best for soaring	**d.** rigid skeleton
_____ **17.** ensure a bird's lungs always have oxygen	**e.** rapidly beating heart
_____ **18.** allow wings to move powerfully and efficiently	**f.** long, narrow wings

Getting off the Ground (p. 378)

19. The upward pressure on the wing that keeps a bird in the air is

called _____ .

Mark each of the following statements *True* or *False*.

20. _____ The top of a bird's wing is curved so air flowing under the wing moves faster than the air flowing over the wing.

21. _____ The larger the wings, the greater the lift.

22. _____ Birds must flap their wings constantly to stay in the air.

Bringing Up Baby (p. 379)

23. Which of the following is NOT true about brooding?

    a. It keeps a bird's eggs warm.
    b. All birds share the responsibility between males and females.
    c. A bird does this until its eggs hatch.
    d. Birds sit on their eggs.

24. How do cuckoos and cowbirds make other birds do their work for them?

_____

_____

_____

Section Review (p. 379)

Now that you've finished Section 1, review what you learned by answering the Section Review questions in your ScienceLog.

Section 2: Kinds of Birds (p. 380)

1. One of the smallest birds is the 1.6 g

bee _____ .

Flightless Birds (p. 380)

2. Look at Figure 9 on page 380. Describe an adaptation that helps each of the following flightless birds get around.

a. Ostriches _____

_____

b. Penguins _____

_____

_____

Water Birds (p. 381)

3. Look at the description of Water Birds on page 381. Water birds

usually have _____ feet for swimming or

_____ legs for wading.

4. What is the blue-footed booby known for?

    a. remaining underwater for long periods of time
    b. attracting females with beautiful plumage
    c. attracting mates with a complicated dance
    d. surviving in polar regions

Birds of Prey (p. 381)

5. Which of the following would NOT be helpful to birds of prey?

    a. very good vision   **c.** sharp, curved beaks
    b. sharp claws   **d.** webbed feet

6. Most birds of prey hunt during the _____ .

Perching Birds (p. 382)

7. Why don't perching birds fall off their perches when they sleep?

_____

_____

_____

8. Chickadees can dangle underneath branches and hunt for food at

the same time. True or False? (Circle one.)

Chapter 14 Directed Reading, continued

Section Review (p. 382)

Now that you've finished Section 2, review what you learned by answering the Section Review questions in your ScienceLog.

Section 3: Characteristics of Mammals (p. 383)

1. The largest animal that has ever lived is a mammal. True or False? (Circle one.)

The First Mammals (p. 383)

2. Reptiles called _____ had characteristics of both mammals and reptiles.

3. Which of the following statements is NOT true about the first mammals?

   a. They appeared in the fossil record about 200 million years ago.
   b. They could look for food at night.
   c. They existed only after dinosaurs became extinct.
   d. They were able to keep a constant body temperature.

Common Characteristics (p. 384)

4. Which of the following statements are true of young mammals? (Circle all that apply.)

   a. They result from sexual reproduction.
   b. They are protected by their parent(s).
   c. They are cared for by one or both parents until they are grown.
   d. They nurse.

5. Mammary glands are special organs that only female mammals have. True or False? (Circle one.)

6. The milk of mammals is made up of fat, water,

   _____ , and _____ .

7. The main purpose of a mammal's diaphragm is to

   a. bring air into the lungs.
   b. separate blood with oxygen from blood without oxygen.
   c. provide as much oxygen as possible to the heart.
   d. make sounds necessary for communication.

8. A mammal often changes its body temperature to help it survive during cold weather. True or False? (Circle one.)

9. Name two adaptations that help keep mammals warm.

   _____

   _____

   _____

▲▲ CHAPTER 14

Chapter 14 Directed Reading, continued

Match the type of tooth in Column B to its use in Column A, and write the corresponding letter in the space provided.

Column A	Column B
_____ **10.** cutting	**a.** canine
_____ **11.** grinding	**b.** incisor
_____ **12.** stabbing	**c.** molar

13. The size and shape of a mammal's _____ match the kind of food it eats.

14. Mammals have _____ sets of teeth.

15. A mammal's large brain allows it to respond quickly to events

around it. True or False? (Circle one.)

Section Review (p. 386)

Now that you've finished Section 3, review what you learned by answering the Section Review questions in your ScienceLog.

Section 4: Kinds of Mammals (p. 387)

1. Some mammals hatch from eggs. True or False? (Circle one.)

Monotremes (p. 387)

2. Why are monotremes considered mammals even though they lay eggs?

_____

_____

_____

_____

_____

_____

3. The platypus and two species of _____ are the only living monotremes. Monotremes are found only in

Australia and _____ .

4. Like other mammals, baby montremes drink milk from their

mother's nipples. True or False? (Circle one.)

Marsupials (p. 388)

5. Marsupials lay eggs like monotremes do. True or False? (Circle one.)

6. Marsupials use their pouches to

    a. store food in the winter.   **c.** feed and protect their young.

    b. give birth to their young.   **d.** digest food for their young.

7. The _____ is the only living marsupial in North America.

Placental Mammals (p. 389)

8. Female placental mammals do NOT

    a. have a uterus.

    b. supply food and oxygen to the embryo through a placenta.

    c. have a gestation period lasting from a few weeks to many months.

    d. lay eggs.

9. All toothless mammals have no teeth. True or False? (Circle one.)

10. Most toothless mammals catch insects with a long, sticky tongue. True or False? (Circle one.)

11. Insectivores are tiny mammals that live on every continent except

_____ and _____ .
Most of them dig in the soil with their long, pointed

_____ .

12. A rodents' teeth don't wear down because they grow continuously.

True or False? (Circle one.)

13. Look at the description of lagomorphs and Figure 26 on page 391. Which of the following is NOT a characteristic of a lagomorph?

    a. sensitive noses   **c.** two sets of teeth

    b. large ears   **d.** long tails

14. Explain how bats use sound to find prey.

_____

_____

_____

_____

_____

▲ ▲ **CHAPTER 14**

15. Animals that eat mostly meat are called

_____ . Meat-eaters have large canines

and special _____ for slicing meat.

16. Some carnivores also eat _____ .

17. Hoofed mammals are divided into orders based on the thickness of their hooves. True or False? (Circle one.)

18. Giraffes are the tallest living mammals. True or False? (Circle one.)

19. Look at page 393. Elephants use their trunk the same

way we use our _____ ,

_____ , and nose.

20. While cetaceans look more like fish than mammals,

they have _____ and they

_____ .

21. Sperm whales are cetaceans that use echolocation to find their food. True or False? (Circle one.)

22. Which of the following characteristics does NOT describe sirenia such as manatees or dugongs?
   a. eat seaweed and water plants
   b. live in the water
   c. are quiet
   d. make up the largest group of mammals

Look at the description of primates on page 395. Then mark each of the following statements *True* or *False*.

23. _____ Monkeys, humans, and prosimians are all primates.

24. _____ Primates have larger brains than other mammals the same size.

25. _____ Primates have forward-facing eyes.

26. _____ All primates have five fingers on each hand and five toes on each foot.

27. _____ All primates live on the ground.

28. _____ All primates have claws.

Section Review (p. 395)

Now that you've finished Section 4, review what you learned by answering the Section Review questions in your ScienceLog.

CHAPTER

15 DIRECTED READING WORKSHEET

Maps as Models of the Earth

As you read Chapter 15, which begins on page 406 of your textbook, answer the following questions.

A Picture of the World (p. 406)

1. Why did ancient maps of the world contain scenes of mythical places and monsters?

_____

_____

_____

_____

2. What do people use to make accurate maps today?

_____

_____

_____

Pre-Reading Questions (p. 406)

Answer these questions in your ScienceLog now. Then later, you'll have a chance to revise your answers based on what you've learned.

Start-Up Activity (p. 407)

3. What two things will you do in this activity?

_____

_____

_____

_____

Section 1: You Are Here (p. 408)

4. How is the map in Figure 1 different from one you might see today?

_____

_____

_____

CHAPTER 15

What Does Earth Really Look Like? (p. 408)

Mark each of the following statements *True* or *False*.

5. _____ Christopher Columbus was the first person to think that the Earth was shaped like a sphere.

6. _____ About 240 BCE, Eratosthenes calculated the Earth's circumference with an error of only 15 percent.

Finding Direction on Earth (p. 409)

7. Because Earth is round, we often describe direction and location using _____ as reference points. (Circle one.)

   a. the North and South Poles   **c.** the stars
   b. the West and East Poles   **d.** none of the above

8. Label the following directions on the diagram: South (S), Southwest (SW), East (E), Northwest (NW), West (W), Southeast (SE), Northeast (NE).

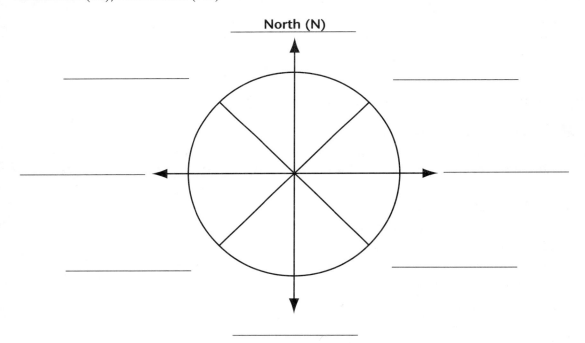

North (N)

9. Magnetic poles and geographic poles are at different locations on the Earth. True or False? (Circle one.)

10. Which kind of pole is true north?

   a. a geologic pole   **c.** a magnetic pole
   b. a geographic pole   **d.** none of the above

11. In order to find true north with a compass, you must use an angle of correction called _____ .

Chapter 15 Directed Reading, continued

Finding Locations on Earth (p. 411)

12. Latitude and longitude are used together to create

_____ addresses.

Mark each of the following statements *True* or *False*.

13. _____ Imaginary lines drawn around the Earth parallel to the equator are called lines of longitude.

14. _____ The equator divides the Earth into the Western and Eastern Hemispheres.

15. _____ All lines of longitude intersect at only two points.

16. _____ Lines of latitude sometimes intersect.

17. The prime meridian
    a. circles the globe like the equator.
    b. runs from the North Pole to the South Pole.
    c. was set at 180° through an international agreement.

18. In Figure 8 on page 413, what line of latitude runs just north of Houston?

_____

19. What line of longitude runs just east of Houston?

_____

Section Review (p. 413)

Now that you've finished Section 1, review what you learned by answering the Section Review questions in your ScienceLog.

Section 2: Mapping Earth's Surface (p. 414)

1. Why it is better to use a map than a globe when studying the Earth's surface? (Circle all that apply.)
    a. Maps show more detail than globes.
    b. Maps can show the whole Earth or parts of it.
    c. Maps are the most accurate models of the Earth.

A Flat Sphere? (p. 414)

2. Changes in the shapes and sizes of landmasses and oceans caused by moving information from a curved surface to a flat surface are

called _____ .

3. Name three geometric shapes on which mapmakers base map projections.

_____

CHAPTER 15

Chapter 15 Directed Reading, continued

After you finish reading pages 415–416, label each of the following as a feature of a Mercator, conic, or azimuthal projection. Write *M* for Mercator, *C* for conic, or *A* for azimuthal.

4. _____ There is little distortion at only one point.

5. _____ It's best for mapping land that has more area east to west than north to south.

6. _____ Distorts distances and sizes of areas near the poles.

7. _____ Shows Earth's latitude and longitude as straight lines.

8. _____ It has no distortion along one line of latitude.

Modern Mapmaking (p. 417)

9. How have airplanes had an effect on mapmaking?

_____

_____

10. A bird's-eye view of the Earth's surface photographed by a camera on a plane is called

    a. a satellite image.   **c.** an aerial photograph.
    b. a Mercator projection.   **d.** none of the above

11. If a scientist collected information about an object while being near the object, we say the scientist used remote sensing.

True or False? (Circle one.)

12. Give two examples of tools used in remote sensing.

_____

_____

_____

13. Satellites gather information about energy coming from Earth's surface. True or False? (Circle one.)

Information Shown on Maps (p. 418)

Use Figure 14 to answer the following questions.

14. The part of a map that lists and explains the symbols used is a

_____ .

15. The subject of the map is given in the _____ .

16. The _____ scale is a bar showing units of distance that represent the distance on Earth's surface.

17. A unitless fraction or ratio that shows the relationship between a distance on the map and a distance on Earth's surface is

called a _____ .

Section Review (p. 419)

Now that you've finished Section 2, review what you learned by answering the Section Review questions in your ScienceLog.

Section 3: Topographic Maps (p. 420)

1. A topographic map would be the best kind of map to use on

    a. a sea cruise.   **c.** a trip to the moon.

    b. a tour of Manhattan.   **d.** a wilderness camping trip.

2. A topographic map shows only natural features, such as rivers,

lakes, and mountains. True or False? (Circle one.)

Elements of Elevation (p. 420)

3. What government agency has made topographic maps for all of the United States? Write out the full name and the abbreviation.

_____

4. In Figure 15, each contour line connects points of equal

_____ .

5. Suppose you are looking at a map that has a small contour interval. What might this tell you about the land?

    a. It is mountainous.   **c.** It has high relief.

    b. It is relatively flat.   **d.** It has steep slopes.

6. If you are hiking on a trail with a steep slope, the contour lines

on your map will be close together. True or False? (Circle one.)

7. An index contour is darker and _____ than other contour lines, and is marked by

_____ .

Reading a Topographic Map (p. 422)

Write the color that indicates each feature on a topographic map.

8. Wooded areas are _____ .

9. Contour lines are _____ .

10. Buildings, roads, bridges, and railroads are

_____ .

11. Major highways are _____ .

Take a look at the legend in Figure 17. Then choose the symbol in Column B that best matches the description in Column A, and write the corresponding letter in the space provided.

Column A	Column B
____ **12.** a school	**a.** ⬭ ◨ ◨
____ **13.** a bridge	**b.** ┼┼┼
____ **14.** a lake or pond	**c.** ┿┿ ┿┿
____ **15.** a railroad track	**d.** ⚑

16. Read the Environment Connection on page 423. Why might the Texas Parks and Wildlife Department use a topographic map?
   a. to look for a street address
   b. to keep track of active volcanoes
   c. to record and protect places where endangered species are
   d. They never use topographic maps.

17. What does it mean when a contour line is V-shaped?

_____

_____

18. Describe a depression on a contour map.

_____

_____

_____

_____

Section Review (p. 423)

Now that you've finished Section 3, review what you learned by answering the Section Review questions in your ScienceLog.

CHAPTER

16 DIRECTED READING WORKSHEET

Rocks

As you read Chapter 16, which begins on page 432 of your textbook, answer the following questions.

Steps for a Giant (p. 433)

1. According to Irish legend, the mythical hero Finn MacCool built

   the _____ as stepping stones to cross the
   sea to invade a neighboring island.

2. How was the Giant's Causeway actually formed?

   _____

   _____

   _____

   _____

Pre-Reading Questions (p. 432)

Answer these questions in your ScienceLog now. Then later, you'll have a chance to revise your answers based on what you've learned.

Start-Up Activity (p. 433)

3. How do scientists classify rocks?

   _____

   _____

Section 1: Types of Rock (p. 434)

4. What is rock?

   _____

   _____

Minerals (p. 434)

5. Every mineral has a unique set of physical properties, such as color and hardness, that are determined by its chemical makeup.

   True or False? (Circle one.)

6. Minerals combine in many ways to form _____ .

Match each mineral in Column A to the description of its physical properties in Column B. Write the corresponding letter in the space provided.

Column A	Column B
_____ **7.** often pink, breaks in two directions	**a.** calcite
_____ **8.** very hard, doesn't break along flat surfaces	**b.** quartz
_____ **9.** metallic-looking, breaks in three directions	**c.** biotite mica
_____ **10.** very soft, breaks in three directions	**d.** orthoclase
_____ **11.** dark brown, breaks in only one direction	**e.** galena

The Nitty-Gritty on Rock Classification (p. 435)

12. The three major types of rock are _____ ,

_____ , and _____ .

13. Metamorphic rock is formed when

  a. hot, liquid rock cools and hardens.
  b. minerals break apart.
  c. rock is heated or squeezed.
  d. rocks are broken down into smaller pieces and harden.

14. The chemical makeup of a rock is called its _____ .

15. A rock with a fine-grained texture is made of large crystals or grains.

  True or False? (Circle one.)

Igneous Rock (p. 436)

16. How does igneous rock form?

  _____

  _____

17. Magma from deep inside the Earth forms

  _____ igneous rocks such as basalt.

18. When magma cools quickly at the surface of the Earth, it forms

  _____ rocks with very small crystals.

Sedimentary Rock (p. 437)

19. When layers of sediment pile up and are squeezed together,

  sedimentary rock is formed. True or False? (Circle one.)

Chapter 16 Directed Reading, continued

20. How are limestone and shale similar? How are they different?

_____

_____

_____

21. What does Figure 7 on page 437 tell you about how sediments can be deposited?

_____

_____

_____

Metamorphic Rock (p. 438)

22. How is metamorphic rock formed?

_____

_____

_____

23. When the mineral grains form bands in a metamorphic rock, the

rock has a _____ texture.

24. Metamorphic rock with grains that line up has a nonfoliated

texture. True or False? (Circle one.)

Section Review (p. 438)

Now that you've finished Section 1, review what you learned by answering the Section Review questions in your ScienceLog.

Section 2: The Rock Cycle (p. 439)

1. The _____ is the name given to the
continual process by which new rock forms from old rock material.

Round and Round It Goes (p. 439)

2. Each type of rock can become any other type of rock. True or False? (Circle one.)

3. When magma cools it forms

    a. metamorphic rock.   **c.** ice.

    b. igneous rock.   **d.** sedimentary rock.

4. Which of the following can break down to form sediment?
(Circle all that apply.)

    a. magma   **c.** igneous rock

    b. metamorphic rock   **d.** sedimentary rock

The Rock Cycle (p. 440)

Use the diagram on pages 440 and 441 to answer questions 5–7 below.

5. Over time, layers of _____ are squeezed
and cemented together to form sedimentary rock.

6. Which kind of rock could be described as being formed by
"pressure cooking"?

_____

_____

7. After metamorphic rock changes to magma, the magma rises and
cools to become

    a. igneous rock.   **c.** metamorphic rock.

    b. sediment.   **d.** sedimentary rock.

Processes That Shape the Earth (p. 442)

8. How does weathering occur?

_____

_____

_____

9. The process by which newly formed sediments are dropped in
low-lying areas is called erosion. True or False? (Circle one.)

10. What can cause rock to metamorphose?

_____

_____

11. How can buried rock be brought to the surface? (Circle all that apply.)

    a. by uplift   **c.** by layers of sediment being
                                 squeezed

    b. when rock melts   **d.** when overlying rocks erode away

Section Review (p. 443)

Now that you've finished Section 2, review what you learned by
answering the Section Review questions in your ScienceLog.

CHAPTER

17 **DIRECTED READING WORKSHEET**

The Restless Earth

As you read Chapter 17, which begins on page 454 of your textbook, answer the following questions.

Road Closed for Repairs! (p. 455)

1. Imagine you are experiencing an earthquake. What does it feel like?

_____

_____

_____

2. How do you think earthquakes are important to scientists?

_____

_____

_____

_____

Pre-Reading Questions (p. 454)

Answer these questions in your ScienceLog now. Then later, you'll have a chance to revise your answers based on what you've learned.

Start-Up Activity (p. 455)

3. What will you do in this activity?

_____

_____

_____

_____

Section 1: Inside the Earth (p. 456)

4. Scientists classify Earth's layers by their _____

and their _____ .

The Composition of the Earth (p. 456)

5. Which of the following is NOT true of oceanic crust?

    a. it is denser than continental crust

    b. it is about 30 km thick

    c. it contains iron, calcium, and magnesium

    d. it is part of the outermost layer of the Earth

6. The mantle is thicker than the crust. True or False? (Circle one.)

7. If you were to dig to the center of the Earth, in what order would you encounter the three major layers?

    a. core, mantle, crust   **c.** crust, mantle, core

    b. mantle, crust, core   **d.** crust, core, mantle

8. Why can underwater volcanoes be called "windows" to the Earth's mantle?

_____

_____

_____

_____

_____

_____

9. Draw a pie chart showing the approximate percentages of Earth's mass in each of Earth's three layers. Use the circle given.

Earth's Mass

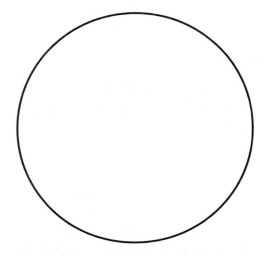

Chapter 17 Directed Reading, continued

The Structure of the Earth (p. 458)

10. Look at the Biology Connection on page 458. Which of the following is included in the biosphere? (Circle all that apply.)

   a. dry land
   b. the upper part of the mantle
   c. the lower part of the atmosphere
   d. the oceans

Complete the table.

	Physical layers of Earth	Physical properties	Thickness (in km)
11.		Hard	60–300
12.		Solid rock that flows	
13.			2,550
14.	Outer core		
15.		Solid and dense	1,228

16. Tectonic plates are part of the ———————————— .

Mapping the Earth's Interior (p. 460)

17. ———————————— produce seismic waves.

18. No one has ever seen the inside of the Earth. How have scientists determined its internal structure?

_____

_____

_____

_____

_____

_____

Section Review (p. 460)

Now that you've finished Section 1, review what you learned by answering the Section Review questions in your ScienceLog.

Section 2: Continents on the Move (p. 461)

1. Tectonic plates move around on the asthenosphere.

True or False? (Circle one.)

Tracking Tectonic Plate Motion (p. 461)

2. The place where two tectonic plates meet is called the

_____ .

3. How does the Global Positioning System (GPS) help scientists measure the rate of tectonic plate movement?

_____

_____

_____

_____

_____

_____

Tectonic Plates (p. 462)

4. Which of the following are characteristics of tectonic plates? (Circle all that apply.)

   a. They do not fit neatly together with surrounding plates.
   b. They are different sizes.
   c. Some have only oceanic crust.
   d. Some include continental and oceanic crust.

5. The South American tectonic plate only has continental crust.

True or False? (Circle one.)

6. A long mountain chain called a _____ is formed where tectonic plates pull apart on the ocean floor.

7. Continental lithosphere displaces more asthenosphere than oceanic lithosphere does. True or False? (Circle one.)

The Changing Earth (p. 464)

8. Millions of years ago, continents were joined together into one large continent, or _____ , called

_____ .

9. What is the supercontinent cycle?

_____

_____

_____

Section Review (p. 464)

Now that you've finished Section 2, review what you learned by answering the Section Review questions in your ScienceLog.

Section 3: Tectonic Forces (p. 465)

1. Certain materials may bend or break depending on how much

_____ is placed on them.

Rocks Get Stressed (p. 465)

2. What is deformation?

_____

_____

3. Which factors determine how much stress a rock can handle before it will bend or break? (Circle all that apply.)

　a. the amount of pressure on the rock
　b. the rock's temperature
　c. the rock's composition
　d. the rock's texture

4. _____ is the type of stress that results when tectonic plates collide, while _____ is the result of tectonic plates pulling away from each other.

Folding (p. 466)

5. Look at the second diagram of Figure 11. If a rock undergoes

horizontal stress, _____ and

_____ will form.

6. If both ends of a fold are still horizontal after folding, the fold is a

_____ .

Faulting (p. 467)

7. Rocks break and slide past each other along a surface called a

fault. True or False? (Circle one.)

8. In Figure 13, a person is leaning against the

_____ , and another person is

suspended from the _____ .

9. In the diagram below, the hanging wall is on the

_____ .

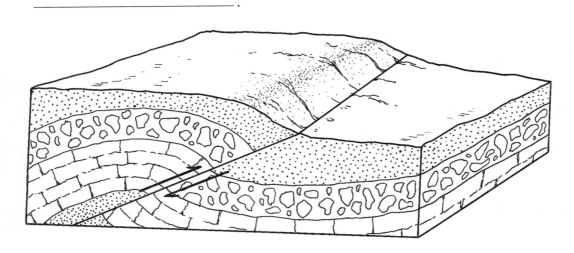

10. The diagram above shows a _____ fault.

11. You can tell the difference between a reverse and a normal fault by
looking at the order of the rock layers. True or False? (Circle one.)

12. A _____ fault occurs when rocks break
and move horizontally due to opposing forces.

Section Review (p. 468)

Now that you've finished Section 3, review what you learned by
answering the Section Review questions in your ScienceLog.

Section 4: Building Mountains (p. 469)

1. What happens when tectonic plates collide?

_____

_____

_____

Uplift (p. 469)

2. A _____ is where two tectonic plates meet
after they collide.

3. What happens to the crust when tectonic plates collide?

_____

_____

_____

_____

4. What are the three most common types of mountains?

_____

_____

_____

_____

5. Look at the Brain Food on page 470. Plate tectonics is responsible for both the world's highest mountains and its deepest valleys

called _____ .

6. When the Appalachian Mountains first formed 390 million years ago, they were located at the boundary between the North

American and African tectonic plates. True or False? (Circle one.)

Write the type of mountain illustrated in each diagram.

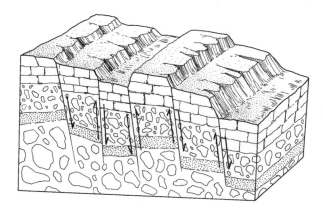

7. _____

8. _____

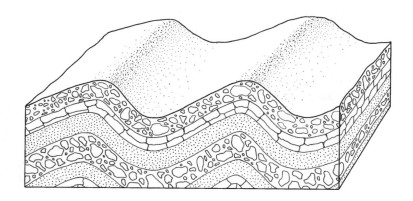

9. _____

Section Review (p. 473)

Now that you've finished Section 4, review what you learned by answering the Section Review questions in your ScienceLog.

CHAPTER

18 DIRECTED READING WORKSHEET

The Flow of Fresh Water

As you read Chapter 18, which begins on page 482 of your textbook, answer the following questions.

The Sound Is Deafening (p. 482)

1. Describe the path of the Iguaçu River.

_____

_____

_____

_____

2. How did the Iguaçu Falls move 28 km upstream?

_____

_____

Pre-Reading Questions (p. 482)

Answer these questions in your ScienceLog now. Then later, you'll have a chance to revise your answers based on what you've learned.

Start-Up Activity (p. 483)

3. This activity models how water flows underground. True or False? (Circle one.)

Section 1: The Active River (p. 484)

4. What process formed the canyon shown in Figure 1?

_____

_____

_____

The Water Cycle (p. 485)

5. Where does the energy that drives the water cycle come from?

_____

_____

_____

CHAPTER 18

Chapter 18 Directed Reading, continued

When you finish reading page 485, choose the term in Column B
that best matches the phase of the water cycle in Column A, and
write the corresponding letter in the appropriate space.

Column A	Column B
_____ **6.** Liquid water from the Earth's surface changes into water vapor.	**a.** precipitation
_____ **7.** Water vapor in the air changes into liquid droplets, forming clouds.	**b.** percolation
_____ **8.** Water falls from clouds to the Earth's surface.	**c.** runoff
_____ **9.** Water flows across the land and enters rivers and streams.	**d.** evaporation
_____ **10.** Water in the ground moves downward through soil due to gravity.	**e.** condensation

River Systems (p. 486)

11. River systems are formed by networks of rivers and streams called

tributaries. True or False? (Circle one.)

12. A region of land drained by a river system is called a

_____ .

13. What is the largest watershed in the United States?

_____

_____

_____

14. Look at Figure 3. The Continental Divide runs through the

    a. Mississippi River.   **c.** Rocky Mountains.
    b. Missouri River.   **d.** Gulf of Mexico.

Stream Erosion (p. 487)

15. How is a river's channel formed?

_____

_____

_____

_____

Chapter 18 Directed Reading, continued

16. A stream with a high gradient is probably on a

_____ , and its water flows rapidly and

has _____ erosive energy.

17. List two things that would cause a stream's discharge to increase.

_____

_____

_____

_____

18. A fast river can carry _____ particles than
a slow river.

19. Look at the illustrations on page 488. A river looks muddy

because of its _____ load.

The Stages of a River (p. 489)

20. Do all rivers erode at the same rate? Why or why not?

_____

_____

_____

_____

_____

21. A mature river flows faster than a youthful river.

True or False? (Circle one.)

Choose the type of river in Column B that best matches the
description in Column A, and write the corresponding letter in the
appropriate space. River types may be used more than once.

Column A	Column B
_____ **22.** high discharge	**a.** youthful river
_____ **23.** flood plains	**b.** mature river
_____ **24.** waterfalls and rapids	**c.** old river
_____ **25.** steplike terraces	**d.** rejuvenated river
_____ **26.** erodes its channel wider, not deeper	

Section Review (p. 490)

Now that you've finished Section 1, review what you learned by answering the Section Review questions in your ScienceLog.

Section 2: Stream and River Deposits (p. 491)

1. Rivers transport soil to farmlands and wetlands. True or False? (Circle one.)

Deposition in Water (p. 491)

2. Deposition destroys productive soil. True or False? (Circle one.)

3. Deposition happens in locations where the current

_____ , such as around the

_____ .

4. If you were a miner in 1850s California, where would you choose to pan for gold?

_____

_____

_____

_____

5. A river can cause a coastline to grow when a

_____ forms.

Deposition on Land (p. 493)

6. Alluvial fans are usually found

   a. at the top of a mountain.
   b. along the side of a mountain.
   c. at the base of a mountain.

7. Suppose you want to buy a farm. Name an advantage and a disadvantage to choosing a farm that is located in a flood plain.

_____

_____

_____

_____

Chapter 18 Directed Reading, continued

Section Review (p. 493)

Now that you've finished Section 2, review what you learned by answering the Section Review questions in your ScienceLog.

Section 3: Water Underground (p. 494)

1. What is ground water?

_____

_____

_____

2. Almost _____ percent of the world's liquid fresh water is stored underground.

The Location of Ground Water (p. 494)

3. After a rainstorm, water passes through the zone of

_____ and collects in the spaces between

rock particles in the zone of _____ .

4. What causes the water table to change?

_____

_____

_____

_____

_____

Aquifers (p. 494)

5. A rock layer that stores ground water and allows it to flow is

called a(n) _____ .

Mark each of the following statements *True* or *False*.

6. _____ A rock is permeable if it stops the flow of water.

7. _____ Aquifers are often formed from sandstone.

8. _____ Some cities obtain their water supply from aquifers.

9. _____ Aquifers release water into recharge zones.

10. _____ Aquifers must have no open spaces.

CHAPTER 18

Springs and Wells (p. 496)

11. Ground water moves toward _____ elevations.

12. Lakes form in areas where the water table is

_____ the Earth's surface.

13. A well can provide water as long as the bottom of the well stays

below the level of the _____ .

Underground Erosion and Deposition (p. 496)

14. How do underground caves form?

_____

_____

_____

_____

Answer the following questions after reading pages 496–497. Choose the term in Column B that best matches the phrase in Column A, and write the corresponding letter in the appropriate space.

Column A	Column B
_____ 15. feature formed when deposits of calcium carbonate from a cave ceiling and floor join together	**a.** stalagmite
_____ 16. icicle-shaped feature that forms on the ceiling of a cave	**b.** stalactite
_____ 17. cone-shaped feature that forms on the floor of a cave	**c.** dripstone column

Section Review (p. 497)

Now that you've finished Section 3, review what you learned by answering the Section Review questions in your ScienceLog.

CHAPTER

19 DIRECTED READING WORKSHEET

The Earth's Atmosphere

As you read Chapter 19, which begins on page 506 of your textbook, answer the following questions.

Floating on Air (p. 506)

1. Why is it necessary that these skydivers know what to expect from the atmosphere?

_____

_____

_____

_____

_____

Pre-Reading Questions (p. 506)

Answer these questions in your ScienceLog now. Then later, you'll have a chance to revise your answers based on what you've learned.

Start-Up Activity (p. 507)

2. What is the purpose of this activity?

_____

_____

Section 1: Characteristics of the Atmosphere (p. 508)

3. Why is the atmosphere important to us? (Circle all that apply.)

    a. It contains the oxygen we breathe.
    b. It keeps the clouds close to the Earth.
    c. It protects us from the sun's harmful rays.
    d. It holds us onto the Earth's surface.

Components of the Atmosphere (p. 508)

Mark each of the following statements *True* or *False*.

4. _____ The atmosphere contains some solids.

5. _____ Oxygen is the most common gas in Earth's atmosphere.

6. _____ Water is the most common liquid in Earth's atmosphere.

▲ ▲ CHAPTER 19
▲

Atmospheric Pressure and Temperature (p. 509)

7. Why do your ears pop when you ride up or down in an elevator in a tall building?

_____

_____

_____

_____

_____

8. Gravity holds the atmosphere around the Earth.

True or False? (Circle one.)

9. Air pressure _____ as you move away from Earth's surface.

10. What is altitude?

_____

_____

11. Differences in temperature between layers of the atmosphere are mainly due to the way the _____ is absorbed by gases as it moves through the atmosphere.

Structure of the Atmosphere (p. 510)

12. In which of the following atmospheric layers does temperature generally decrease as altitude increases? (Circle all that apply.)

    a. troposphere   **c.** mesosphere
    b. stratosphere   **d.** thermosphere

13. Most of the mass of the Earth's atmosphere is in the

_____ .

14. You live in the troposphere. True or False? (Circle one.)

15. Take a look at Figure 4 on page 511. Ozone is made up of oxygen atoms. How is ozone different from the oxygen you breathe?

_____

_____

_____

_____

16. The ozone in the atmosphere absorbs _____ .

17. The coldest layer of the atmosphere is the

    a. troposphere.   **c.** mesosphere.

    b. stratosphere.   **d.** thermosphere.

18. The thermosphere isn't a hot place, even though it has very high temperatures. Why?

_____

_____

_____

_____

_____

_____

_____

_____

19. Ions are electrically charged particles. True or False? (Circle one.)

20. The ionosphere _____ radio signals.

Section Review (p. 513)

Now that you've finished Section 1, review what you learned by answering the Section Review questions in your ScienceLog.

Section 2: Heating of the Atmosphere (p. 514)

1. The Earth's atmosphere is heated by the sun's energy.

    True or False? (Circle one.)

Energy in the Atmosphere (p. 514)

2. The Earth receives about _____ of the radiation released by the sun.

3. Take a moment to look at Figure 7. What percentage of the sun's energy that reaches the Earth is absorbed or reflected in each of the following ways?

_____ absorbed by the Earth's surface

_____ absorbed by ozone, clouds, and atmospheric gases

Chapter 19 Directed Reading, continued

4. Energy transferred by heat from the sidewalk to your foot is an example

   of _____ .

5. In convection currents, cool air _____ .

The Greenhouse Effect (p. 516)

6. Take a look at Figure 9. How do greenhouse gases act like the layer
   of glass in a greenhouse?

   _____

   _____

   _____

   _____

Mark each of the following statements *True* or *False.*

7. _____ An increase in the greenhouse effect would not cause
   global warming.

8. _____ The balance between incoming energy and outgoing
   energy is called the radiation balance.

9. Why would planting millions of trees help reduce the greenhouse
   effect?

   _____

   _____

   _____

   _____

Section Review (p. 517)

Now that you've finished Section 2, review what you learned by
answering the Section Review questions in your ScienceLog.

Section 3: Atmospheric Pressure and Winds (p. 518)

1. The damage in Figure 11 was caused by the movement of air.

   True or False? (Circle one.)

Why Air Moves (p. 518)

2. Differences in air pressure produce wind. True or False? (Circle one.)

3. Air pressure is high at the _____ because the

   air is _____ there.

4. What produces pressure belts?

_____

_____

5. The winds in the Southern Hemisphere curve to the right due to the Coriolis effect. True or False? (Circle one.)

6. In Figure 13 on page 520, what happens if you try to roll a marble across a spinning Lazy Susan?

_____

_____

_____

Cyclones and Anticyclones (p. 521)

7. Areas with lower pressure than the surrounding areas are called

_____ . Areas with higher pressure are

called _____ .

8. As warm air cools in a cyclone, it forms clouds and rain.
True or False? (Circle one.)

9. Meteorologists predict the weather by keeping track of cyclones
and anticyclones. True or False? (Circle one.)

Kinds of Winds (p. 522)

10. Which of the following is NOT true of local winds?
   a. They are caused by the unequal heating of the Earth's surface
      and pressure differences.
   b. They can blow from any direction.
   c. They usually move short distances.
   d. They are part of a pattern of air flow that moves across the Earth.

Complete the following questions after reading pages 522–524.

11. The word *doldrums* comes from an Old English word that means
   "foolish." Why were the doldrums given that name?

_____

_____

_____

_____

▲ ▲ **CHAPTER 19**

12. The areas of high pressure at 30° north and 30° south latitude are

called the _____ .

13. How can knowing about the jet stream help a pilot?

_____

_____

Choose the global winds in Column B that best match the description in Column A, and write the corresponding letter in the space provided.

Column A	Column B
____ **14.** winds that blow toward the poles between 30° and 60° latitude in both hemispheres	**a.** polar easterlies
____ **15.** narrow belt of high-speed, high-altitude winds that changes paths around the Earth	**b.** westerlies
____ **16.** winds moving from the poles toward 60° latitude in both hemispheres	**c.** trade winds
____ **17.** winds that blow from 30° latitude to the equator	**d.** jet streams

Look at Figure 18 on page 524, and then answer the following questions about sea breezes and land breezes.

18. In the afternoon on the beach, after the sun has heated the land,

you can feel _____ breezes.

19. Sea breezes and land breezes are created because air moves from areas

of high pressure to areas of low pressure. True or False? (Circle one.)

Look at Figure 19 on page 525, and then answer the following questions about mountain and valley breezes.

20. In the afternoon in the mountains, after the sun has heated the

valley floor all day, you can feel a _____
breeze.

21. Mountain breezes and valley breezes are created because warm

air rises and cold air sinks. True or False? (Circle one.)

Section Review (p. 525)

Now that you've finished Section 3, review what you learned by answering the Section Review questions in your ScienceLog.

CHAPTER

20 DIRECTED READING WORKSHEET

Our Solar System

As you read Chapter 20, which begins on page 536 of your textbook, answer the following questions.

A Place of Extremes (p. 536)

1. What is Jupiter's Great Red Spot?

_____

_____

_____

_____

2. What are Io, Europa, Ganymede, and Callisto?

_____

_____

Pre-Reading Questions (p. 536)

Answer these questions in your ScienceLog now. Then later, you'll have a chance to revise your answers based on what you've learned.

Start-Up Activity (p. 537)

3. What is the purpose of this activity?

_____

_____

_____

Section 1: A Solar Family (p. 538)

4. The planets, the _____, and many smaller objects make up our solar system.

The Nine Planets: A Sense of Scale (p. 538)

Look at Figure 1 on pages 538–539. Then mark each of the following statements *True* or *False*.

5. _____ Saturn is larger than Jupiter.

6. _____ Mercury is the smallest planet.

7. _____ The sun is larger than any of the planets.

8. _____ Earth and Venus are about the same size.

▲▲ CHAPTER 20

Measuring Interplanetary Distances (p. 539)

9. About how many kilometers are there in one astronomical unit?

_____

_____

10. Light travels 300,000 km in _____ .

11. Distances in the solar system always must be measured in light-years.
True or False? (Circle one.)

Planetary Motion (p. 540)

12. The objects in the solar system move according to strict physical

laws. True or False? (Circle one.)

Choose the definition in Column B that best matches the term in
Column A, and write the corresponding letter in the space provided.

Column A	Column B
____ **13.** orbit ____ **14.** rotation ____ **15.** period of revolution ____ **16.** revolution	**a.** the amount of time it takes for a single trip around the sun **b.** the spin of an object in space **c.** the motion of a body as it travels around another body in space **d.** the path of a body traveling around another body in space

17. The Earth rotates around the sun. True or False? (Circle one.)

Mid-Section Review (p. 540)

Now that you've finished the first part of Section 1, review what you
learned by answering the Mid-Section Review questions in your
ScienceLog.

The Sun: Head of the Family (p. 541)

18. The sun has a solid surface. True or False? (Circle one.)

19. List the layers of the sun in order from the innermost layer to the
outermost layer.

_____

_____

_____

Chapter 20 Directed Reading, continued

Match each of the terms in Column B with the correct description in Column A, and write the corresponding letter in the space provided. Use Figure 4 to help you. Terms may be used more than once.

Column A	Column B
____ **20.** where the sun's energy is produced	**a.** core
____ **21.** the sun's outer atmosphere	**b.** radiative zone
____ **22.** where atoms are very closely packed	**c.** convective zone
____ **23.** where hot and cool gases circulate	**d.** photosphere
____ **24.** deep-red; visible only with special equipment	**e.** chromosphere
____ **25.** the visible surface of the sun	**f.** corona
____ **26.** can extend outward a distance equal to 10–12 times the sun's diameter	

27. Which of the following are incorrect explanations for the source of the sun's energy? (Circle all that apply.)

    a. The sun is burning fuel to generate energy.

    b. The sun is shrinking.

    c. The sun gets its energy from nuclear fusion.

28. What did Einstein show about matter and energy?

_____

_____

_____

29. Einstein's formula states that energy equals

    a. mass times the speed of light.

    b. mass times the square of the particles of light.

    c. mass times the square of the speed of light.

30. _____ is the process by which two or more low-mass _____ join together to form a _____ massive nucleus.

CHAPTER 20

Solar Activity (p. 544)

31. Sunspots are not really spots on the sun. What are they?

_____

_____

_____

_____

32. The number of sunspots on our sun
   a. is steadily decreasing.
   b. remains the same each year.
   c. changes in a regular cycle.
   d. is steadily increasing.

33. Solar flares are giant _____ on the sun's surface.

34. What are auroras?

_____

_____

_____

_____

Section Review (p. 544)

Now that you've finished Section 1, review what you learned by answering the Section Review questions in your ScienceLog.

Section 2: The Nine Planets (p. 545)

1. What did Galileo Galilei realize in 1610?

_____

_____

_____

The Inner Planets (p. 545)

2. In general, how are the inner planets different from the outer planets? (Circle all that apply.)
   a. They are not spherical.
   b. They are smaller (except for Pluto).
   c. They are dense and rocky, whereas the outer planets, except for icy Pluto, are made mostly of gas.
   d. They are more closely spaced than the outer planets.

Chapter 20 Directed Reading, continued

3. Which group of planets does Earth belong to?

_____

_____

_____

Complete the following section after reading pages 545–549. Be sure to examine the statistics for each planet. Each of the statements refers to an inner planet. In the space provided, write *ME* for Mercury, *V* for Venus, *E* for Earth, or *MA* for Mars.

4. _____ This is the only planet besides Earth with some form of water.

5. _____ This is the only planet we know of that supports life.

6. _____ This planet rotates in a clockwise direction.

7. _____ This planet has the biggest range in surface temperatures.

8. _____ The largest mountain in the solar system is on this planet.

9. _____ On this planet, the sun rises in the west and sets in the east.

10. _____ This planet has the densest atmosphere of all the inner planets.

11. _____ This planet's air pressure is the same as it is 30 km above Earth's surface.

12. _____ This planet revolves around the sun once every 88 Earth days.

13. _____ Water on this planet supports life.

14. What is the goal of NASA's Earth Science Enterprise? (Circle all that apply.)

   a. to study the effects that humans have in changing the global environment
   b. to study whether life is possible on Mars
   c. to get away from Earth
   d. to study Earth as a global system made of smaller systems

Mid-Section Review (p. 549)

Now that you've finished the first part of Section 2, review what you learned by answering the Mid-Section Review questions in your ScienceLog.

▲ CHAPTER 20

The Outer Planets (p. 550)

15. Why are most of the outer planets called gas giants?

_____

_____

_____

_____

Complete the following section after reading pages 550–554. Choose the planet in Column B that matches the description in Column A, and write the corresponding letter in the space provided. Planets may be used more than once.

Column A	Column B
_____ **16.** Like Jupiter, this planet is made mostly of hydrogen and helium.	**a.** Jupiter
_____ **17.** This planet is covered by frozen nitrogen.	**b.** Saturn
_____ **18.** Its moon is more than half its size.	**c.** Uranus
_____ **19.** Clouds of water, methane, and ammonia make up the outer part of this planet's atmosphere.	**d.** Neptune
_____ **20.** This planet may have been tipped over when it was hit by a massive object.	**e.** Pluto
_____ **21.** The Great Dark Spot is on this planet.	
_____ **22.** This planet has a blue-green color.	
_____ **23.** This planet's atmosphere contains belts of visible clouds.	
_____ **24.** Like Jupiter, this planet radiates much more energy into space than it receives from the sun.	
_____ **25.** This planet has the largest rings.	

Section Review (p. 554)

Now that you've finished Section 2, review what you learned by answering the Section Review questions in your ScienceLog.

Section 3: Moons and Other Bodies (p. 555)

1. Many of the moons, comets, asteroids, and meteoroids in our solar system have changed a lot since they first formed.

   True or False? (Circle one.)

Moons (p. 555)

2. What is the difference between a moon and a satellite?

   _____

   _____

   _____

3. Which planets do not have moons?

   a. Mercury and Venus   **c.** Uranus and Neptune
   b. Neptune and Pluto   **d.** Mars and Pluto

Mark each of the following statements *True* or *False*.

4. _____ The rocks brought back from Earth's moon during the Apollo missions were found to be about 4.6 billion years old.

5. _____ The missions to Earth's moon have not given us any information about other parts of the solar system.

6. Phobos and Deimos are moons of Mars. Where do scientists think these moons come from, and why?

   _____

   _____

   _____

   _____

7. Ganymede is the largest of Jupiter's 18 known moons. It is larger than

   a. Mercury.   **c.** Earth.
   b. Venus.   **d.** Mars.

▲▲ CHAPTER 20

8. Europa is another of Jupiter's moons. Why do scientists wonder if life could exist on Europa?

_____

_____

_____

_____

_____

Complete the following section after reading pages 557–558. Write the number of known moons of each planet in the space provided.

9. _____ Neptune

10. _____ Saturn

11. _____ Uranus

12. _____ Pluto

Choose the moon in Column B that best matches the description in Column A, and write the corresponding letter in the space provided.

Column A	Column B
____ **13.** revolves in a backward orbit	**a.** Titan
____ **14.** hazy orange atmosphere containing nitrogen, methane, and other gases	**b.** Charon
____ **15.** patchwork terrain of plains, grooves, and cliffs	**c.** Miranda
____ **16.** period of revolution is 6.4 days long	**d.** Triton

Mid-Section Review (p. 558)

Now that you've finished the first part of Section 3, review what you learned by answering the Mid-Section Review questions in your ScienceLog.

Other Small Bodies (p. 559)

17. Name two objects in the solar system besides moons and planets.

_____

_____

_____

Chapter 20 Directed Reading, continued

18. What are "dirty snowballs," and why are they given that name?

_____

_____

_____

_____

19. Comets can have more than one tail. True or False? (Circle one.)

20. How are the orbits of comets different from the orbits of planets?

_____

_____

_____

_____

21. Where would you most likely find asteroids?

_____

_____

_____

_____

22. Asteroids have a variety of sizes, shapes, and compositions.

True or False? (Circle one.)

23. In the outer region of the asteroid belt, asteroids have dark surfaces.

These asteroids may be rich in _____ .

24. Asteroids closest to the sun are

    a. rich in carbon.
    b. stony or metallic in composition.
    c. rich in organic matter.
    d. dark gray surfaces.

25. Where do scientists think asteroids came from?

_____

_____

_____

_____

▲ ▶ **CHAPTER 20**

26. What is the main difference between a meteoroid and an asteroid?

_____

_____

_____

_____

Mark each of the following statements *True* or *False*.

27. _____ A meteorite is a meteoroid that enters Earth's atmosphere and hits the ground.

28. _____ A meteor shower happens when Earth passes through the dusty debris that comets leave behind.

29. _____ All meteorites are made up of the same types of materials.

30. _____ A meteor is a small, rocky body orbiting the sun.

31. When do we see shooting stars?

_____

_____

_____

_____

32. The three major types of meteorites are

_____.

33. Which type of meteorite may contain organic minerals and water?

  a. stony
  b. metallic
  c. stony-iron

Section Review (p. 561)

Now that you've finished Section 3, review what you learned by answering the Section Review questions in your ScienceLog.

CHAPTER

21 DIRECTED READING WORKSHEET

Exploring Space

As you read Chapter 21, which begins on page 570 of your textbook, answer the following questions.

A Shuttle to Outer Space (p. 570)

1. What is the benefit of a reusable shuttle?

_____

_____

2. What will information gathered from space missions eventually help humans to do?

_____

_____

_____

_____

Pre-Reading Questions (p. 570)

Answer these questions in your ScienceLog now. Then later, you'll have a chance to revise your answers based on what you've learned.

Start-Up Activity (p. 571)

3. How does a rocket work?

_____

_____

_____

Section 1: Rocket Science (p. 572)

4. How did Jules Verne send his fictional character to the moon?

_____

_____

The Beginning of Rocket Science (p. 572)

5. _____ is known as the father of rocket theory, and American physicist _____ became known as the father of modern rocketry.

From Rocket Bombs to Rocket Ships (p. 573)

6. V-2 rocket designer Wernher von Braun and his whole research team surrendered to the Americans near the end of World War II.

True or False? (Circle one.)

7. Why was NASA formed?

_____

_____

_____

_____

How Rockets Work (p. 574)

8. State the principle of physics that explains how rockets work.

_____

_____

9. _____ is the force that accelerates a rocket.

10. In Figure 4, the hot gases in the _____ chamber are under very high pressure.

11. For a rocket to move skyward, what must become greater than the weight of the rocket?
   a. the weight of the air pushing under the rocket
   b. the force of the gas exiting at the bottom of the rocket
   c. the force of the gas pushing against the top of the combustion chamber

12. A rocket must reach a speed of 8 km/s in order to break away from Earth's gravitational pull. True or False? (Circle one.)

13. Why must rockets carry oxygen when traveling into space?

_____

_____

_____

_____

Section Review (p. 575)

Now that you've finished Section 1, review what you learned by answering the Section Review questions in your ScienceLog.

Section 2: Artificial Satellites (p. 576)

1. The Soviet Union launched an artificial satellite before the United States did. True or False? (Circle one.)

The Space Race Begins (p. 576)

Choose the satellite in Column B that is described in Column A, and write the corresponding letter in the space provided.

Column	Column B
_____ **2.** a satellite that carried a dog	**a.** *Sputnik 1*
_____ **3.** the first human-made object to be placed in orbit around the Earth	**b.** *Explorer 1*
_____ **4.** discovered the Van Allen radiation belts	**c.** *Sputnik 2*

Into the Information Age (p. 577)

5. *Tiros 1* was the first United States weather satellite.

True or False? (Circle one.)

6. The first United States _____ satellite was *Echo 1*.

Choose Your Orbit (p. 577)

7. What is LEO?

    a. limited Earth orbit   **c.** low Earth orbit
    b. low emission orbit   **d.** low Earth operation

8. How does a satellite in geosynchronous orbit (GEO) help with your television's reception of a program?

_____

_____

_____

_____

_____

_____

_____

Results of the Satellite Programs (p. 578)

9. Using satellites, scientists have been able to gather information

   by _____ sensing—the gathering of
   information from high above the Earth's surface.

10. Because the Cold War is over, the United States no longer uses spy

    satellites for military defense. True or False? (Circle one.)

11. According to the Environment Connection on page 578, what
    branch of the military tracks "space junk"?

    _____

    _____

    _____

12. What have remote-sensing projects such as Landsat allowed
    scientists to do? (Circle all that apply.)
    a. map the spread of cities
    b. map the surface of the sun
    c. look at changes in vegetation growth
    d. study the effect of humans on the global environment

Section Review (p. 579)

Now that you've finished Section 2, review what you learned by
answering the Section Review questions in your ScienceLog.

Section 3: Space Probes (p. 580)

1. What is the difference between a space probe and a satellite?

   _____

   _____

   _____

   _____

Visits to Our Planetary Neighborhood (p. 580)

Mark each of the following statements *True* or *False*.

2. _____ The first space probe was launched by the Soviets.

3. _____ *Luna 3* made the first soft landing on the moon.

4. _____ *Clementine* discovered possible evidence of water at
   the south pole of the moon.

5. What have we learned about Venus from space probes? (Circle all that apply.)

    a. The surface rocks are very different from those on Earth.

    b. The surface temperature and atmospheric pressure are much higher than on Earth.

    c. The planet has volcanoes.

    d. Some type of plate tectonics happens there.

Choose the Mars space probe from Column B that best matches the description in Column A, and write the corresponding letter in the space provided. Probes may be used more than once.

Column	Column B
_____ **6.** released *Sojourner* rover	**a.** *Viking 2*
_____ **7.** looked for signs of life on Mars	**b.** *Mars Pathfinder*
_____ **8.** showed that Martian exploration is possible at a lower cost than that of the larger missions	
_____ **9.** found signs that Mars was once much warmer and wetter than it is now	

10. *Pioneer 10* and *Pioneer 11* studied the flow of charged particles

coming from the sun called _____ .

11. What was the first space probe to go past Pluto's orbit and in what year it did do so?

_____

_____

12. Where are the *Pioneer* and *Voyager* space probes today?

_____

_____

_____

13. What are two of the exciting things that *Galileo* has discovered about Jupiter's moons?

_____

_____

_____

Space Probes—A New Approach (p. 584)

14. What is NASA's new approach to space probes?

_____

_____

_____

Mark each of the following statements *True* or *False*.

15. _____ The *Stardust* probe will gather samples of a comet's dust tail and return the dust to Earth.

16. _____ NASA is no longer testing any new technologies.

17. What is so unusual about the method of propulsion used in *Deep Space 1*?

_____

_____

_____

_____

18. The *Cassini* probe is being sent to Saturn to make a grand tour of the planet's moons. True or False? (Circle one.)

19. Which of the following is NOT a proposal for a future mission into space?

    a. a space-probe visit to the sun
    b. an orbiter for Europa
    c. an orbiter for Mercury
    d. a space-probe visit to Pluto

Section Review (p. 585)

Now that you've finished Section 3, review what you learned by answering the Section Review questions in your ScienceLog.

Section 4: Living and Working in Space (p. 586)

1. The goal of the Mercury program was to put a man on the moon.

True or False? (Circle one.)

Human Space Exploration (p. 586)

2. The first human to orbit Earth was Soviet cosmonaut

_____ , in the year _____ .

Chapter 21 Directed Reading, continued

3. Why was John F. Kennedy's announcement about sending a person to the moon such a surprise?

_____

_____

_____

_____

4. The first human to set foot on the moon was American astronaut Neil Armstrong, in the year 1972. True or False? (Circle one.)

5. What did *Apollo 11* bring back from the moon?

_____

_____

The Space Shuttle (p. 587)

6. Which of the following does NOT describe a space shuttle?
   a. It is a reusable vehicle.
   b. It lands like a helicopter.
   c. It takes off like a rocket.
   d. It is cheaper than previous ways of getting into space.

7. How did the explosion of the space shuttle *Challenger* affect the space shuttle program?

_____

_____

_____

8. NASA is working on a _____ called the *X33*.

Space Stations—People Working in Space (p. 588)

9. The Soviet Union's space-station program helped people learn more about the effects of _____ on humans.

7. In the Biology Connection on page 588, what effect does staying in space for long periods of time have on bones and muscles?

_____

_____

_____

11. Why did *Skylab* fall into the ocean?

_____

_____

_____

_____

_____

_____

_____

12. Which of the following have NOT been conducted on *Mir*?
   a. manufacturing tests
   b. biological experiments
   c. astronomical studies
   d. All of the above have been conducted on *Mir*.

13. Only Russian cosmonauts have been allowed to live and work on the *Mir* space station. True or False? (Circle one.)

The International Space Station (p. 590)
14. How is the International Space Station being built?

_____

_____

_____

The Moon, Mars, and Beyond (p. 591)
15. What will be the key to colonizing the moon?
   a. making these missions economically worthwhile
   b. using helium in nuclear reactors
   c. establishing recreational uses
   d. developing more technology

Section Review (p. 591)
Now that you've finished Section 4, review what you learned by answering the Section Review questions in your ScienceLog.

NOTES

DATE	NOTES

NOTES

DATE	NOTES